# Reading

Which is first, and which is last,
and which are in the middle?
The magic hat can rearrange
and solve every word riddle.

Rearrange each set of syllables to form a word that makes sense. Write each word in its hat. Then color the hats with 3-syllable words—red, 4-syllable words—blue, and 5-syllable words—yellow.

IF8784 Second Grade in Review

# Reading

Name _____

Robbie Robot, a base model,
is simple and quite plain.
Add new parts, and you will see
what his deluxe model does contain.

Write the base word for each word listed. Then be creative and draw
something on Robbie that the base word suggests.

**Example:** flies _____ (Draw wings on or flies buzzing around Robbie.)

**Robbie Robot**

| | | | | | |
|---|---|---|---|---|---|
| hairy | _____ | bolted | _____ | switches | _____ |
| nosey | _____ | springing | _____ | ringing | _____ |
| smiling | _____ | hats | _____ | heartless | _____ |
| lightest | _____ | buttoned | _____ | wired | _____ |
| doors | _____ | numbers | _____ | shirtless | _____ |

# Reading

Name _____

Follow directions carefully.
Then you will know
what to do next
or which way to go!

Follow the directions in each box. Then use the words to answer the riddles below.

| | |
|---|---|
| 1. Write the name of an insect that is often mistaken for a butterfly. Then write "er" after the name.<br><br>_____ | 2. Write the name of a popular pet. Change the vowel to make the name of a sore.<br><br>_____ |
| 3. Write the word that is the opposite of good. Cross out the vowel. Write the fifth letter of the alphabet above the crossed-out letter.<br><br>_____ | 4. Write the word that is the opposite of walk. Cross out the first consonant. Change it to the 19th letter of the alphabet.<br><br>_____ |
| 5. Write the word that means the opposite of out. To the left of that word write the two-letter abbreviation for company.<br><br>_____ | 6. Write the word that is the opposite of bad. Cross off the final consonant. After the last vowel, write the abbreviation for southeast.<br><br>_____ |

a. What honks but is not a car? _____

b. What can a woman be that a man never can be? _____

c. What has a head and tail but does not have a body? _____

d. What can hurt or shorten? _____

e. What is like a ball that can't be bounced? _____

f. What has a head and four legs but has only one foot? _____

3     IF8784 Second Grade in Review

# Reading

Name _____

Hey, Mister,
What's the scoop?
Does it really
belong in that group?

Cross out the word in each group that does not belong. Then write the headline that best describes the remaining words in that group.

---

**Headlines**

| | | |
|---|---|---|
| Whole Holes | Flights in Space | Doggone It! |
| Going Around in Circles | Let's Run | Just Desserts! |
| Make Me Laugh! | Veggie Power | Legs Are Us |

---

| | | |
|---|---|---|
| giraffe | doughnut | box |
| elephant | door | wheel |
| snake | inner tube | Frisbee |
| ostrich | Lifesaver | hockey puck |

| | | |
|---|---|---|
| Tabby | ice cream | tag |
| Poodle | pie | races |
| Dalmatian | potatoes | jog |
| Irish setter | cake | chess |

| | | |
|---|---|---|
| clown | watermelon | rocket ship |
| joke | peas | cloud |
| house | spinach | jet |
| cartoon | carrots | Superman |

# Reading

People can be funny!
In what little way?
Have you carefully listened
to what they may say?

**Idioms** are funny expressions that people say to "make a point."

Read each idiom and draw a funny picture about it. Then write a sentence that tells what the idiom is supposed to mean.

| | |
|---|---|
| **Example:** <br> It's raining cats and dogs! | He has a green thumb. |
| Time flies! | Did you catch the train? |
| Button your lip! | She has a frog in her throat. |
| You really put your foot in your mouth! | Stop pulling my leg! |

# Reading

Name _____

Kay G. Detective needed to choose
all of the important clues.
When she went on an ocean cruise,
she discovered exciting news!

Kay found this letter taped to her cabin door. Read it and answer the questions.

Dear Miss Detective,

When I awoke at sunrise, I found a very special guest
hiding in my room. At first, I thought I might dye, but now
I no better. I promised to take him to the Emerald Island when
our ship passes it in mid-afternoon.

Please don't get soar, but I need your help! If you
follow my directions carefully, we can help my new friend.

1. Lift up your bed.
2. Crawl through the special tunnel underneath.
3. Walk down a dozen steps. We will be waiting for
   you at the bottom with a raft.

sincerely,
Bea Friend

P.S. I misspelled three words to give you a clue about my guest.

1. About what time did Bea discover
   her uninvited guest?
   a. 6:00 A.M.
   b. 10:00 A.M.
   c. 5:00 P.M.

2. Where were Kay G. and Bea?
   a. on an airplane
   b. on a cruise ship
   c. on an island

3. What three words were spelled
   incorrectly in the letter?

   _____

   _____

   _____

4. What had Bea found in her
   cabin?

   _____

# Reading

Name _____

Ivan Openmind will often pause
to think what really was the cause,
while Seymour Clearly's thoughts must collect
to see what became the effect.

Choose from the **causes** or the **effects** to complete each sentence.

### Ivan Openmind's Causes

Because Otto McCanic made a slight mistake, . . .

When Miss B.U. Tifful forgot to wear makeup, . . .

Because Lotta Suds put too much soap in the washing machine, . . .

### Seymour Clearly's Effects

she handed in her dad's blueprints as homework.

the robot could do her chores and homework while she relaxed.

his cats barked and his dogs meowed.

the director of the play had a fit.

1. _____
   the laundry room was filled with bubbles.

2. When Ken L. Keeper mixed up the dog and cat food, _____
   _____

3. _____
   the car could only go backwards.

4. Because Ima Genius invented a robot, _____
   _____

5. Because Flora Getfull grabbed the wrong papers off the desk, _____
   _____

6. When Otto B. Estar forgot his lines again, _____
   _____

7. _____
   her fans didn't recognize her.

# Reading

Name _____

A **fact** is real,
while **fiction** is not.
Place each phrase below
in the right spot.

Write the number of each phrase on a windowsill in the proper building. Then draw its picture in the window.

1. giant with three eyes
2. round basketball
3. spotted dog
4. chocolate sundae
5. purple monkey
6. wide-screen television

7. frog prince
8. flying cat
9. magic lamp
10. mother and father
11. shiny bicycle
12. fire-breathing dragon

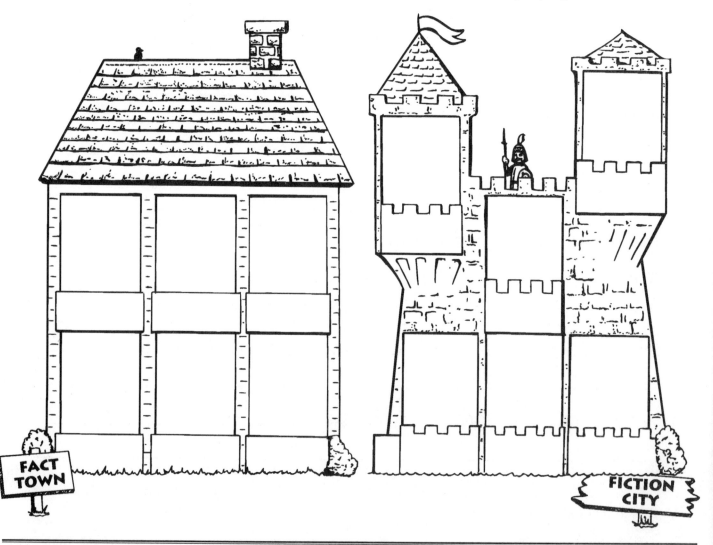

FACT TOWN

FICTION CITY

IF8784 Second Grade in Review

# Reading

Name _____

How does dragon relate to cave,
or queen relate to king?
How does knight relate to night?
Let's do some careful thinking.

**Analogies** show how words are related.

Example: **Dragon** is to **cave** as **bear** is to **den**.

Put on your thinking cap and write the missing word to each analogy.

1. **Fingers** are to **hands** as **toes** are to _____ .
2. **Box** is to **square** as **globe** is to _____ .
3. **Milk** is to **drink** as **bread** is to _____ .
4. **Laugh** is to **happy** as **cry** is to _____ .
5. **Run** is to **ran** as **draw** is to _____ .
6. **Lion** is to **jungle** as **fish** is to _____ .
7. **Mother** is to **father** as **sister** is to _____ .
8. **Crayon** is to **draw** as **pencil** is to _____ .
9. **Run** is to **walk** as **play** is to _____ .
10. **Day** is to **week** as **month** is to _____ .
11. **Scale** is to **weigh** as **ruler** is to _____ .
12. **Teacher** is to **school** as **nurse** is to _____ .
13. **Dog** is to **puppy** as **cat** is to _____ .
14. **Apple** is to **red** as **banana** is to _____ .
15. **Car** is to **garage** as **jet** is to _____ .

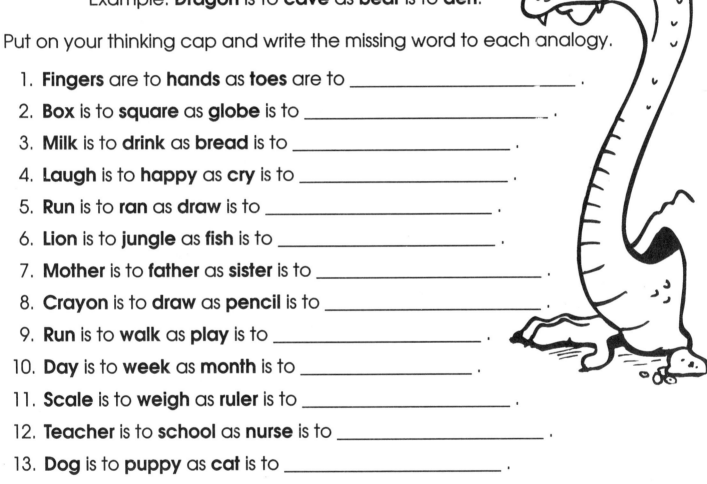

| Word Bank | | | | |
|---|---|---|---|---|
| drew | work | round | write | sea |
| year | hangar | hospital | measure | yellow |
| brother | eat | feet | kitten | sad |

IF8784 Second Grade in Review

# Reading

Elongated words
make one shiver and shake,
but if you read everything else
they're a piece of cake!

Carefully read the story on this and the next page. Fill in the missing words in the story by picking the words in the box that mean the same as the words beneath the lines. **Hint:** It helps to read past the missing word to understand the meaning.

| | | |
|---|---|---|
| (1) near, far away | (11) little, green | (21) exactly, double |
| (2) thought, known | (12) tongue, bite | (22) enemy, friend |
| (3) small, horrible | (13) good, sour | (23) strong, nice |
| (4) lived in, hated | (14) giggle, cry | (24) friendly, nasty |
| (5) huge, tiny | (15) alone, happy | (25) wisely, easily |
| (6) ran, yelled | (16) worry, laugh | (26) frowned, smiled |
| (7) eaten, met | (17) buy, eat | (27) spread, stopped |
| (8) story, bells | (18) nearing, leaving | (28) bothered, liked |
| (9) pile, group | (19) hit, covered | |
| (10) met, hopped | (20) brave, tired | |

Long ago in a (1) _____ kingdom on the other side of the world, it
(remote)

was (2) _____ that a mean and (3) _____
(rumored)                                    (horrendous)

giant and his large family (4) _____ a (5) _____
(inhabited)                        (mammoth)

castle. Whenever thundering footsteps shook the ground, people quickly (6)

_____ in the opposite direction. No one had actually
(scampered)

(7) _____ the giant, but everyone seemed to have heard
(encountered)

the (8) _____ .
(narrative)

One day a (9) _____ of children (10) _____
(cluster)                                      (assembled)

near the giant's castle. They all began teasing a (11) _____
(diminutive)

boy named PeeWee.

# Reading

Name _____

(Continued)

"You're so tiny that you'd hardly make an itty-bitty (12) _____
                                                                    (morsel)

in the giant's mouth!" yelled Sluggo. "I bet you wouldn't even taste

(13) _____ ."
         (palatable)

Poor little PeeWee began to quietly (14) _____ . Then the
                                                 (blubber)

other children ran away, leaving the sad, little boy (15) _____ .
                                                              (solitary)

PeeWee began to (16) _____ about the giant.
                          (fret)

"What if he wants to (17) _____ me?" he thought.
                              (devour)

Suddenly, PeeWee heard footsteps (18) _____ . He
                                             (approaching)

(19) _____ his eyes with his hands.
         (enveloped)

After a minute he became (20) _____ enough to open his
                                    (dauntless)

eyes. Standing before him was a boy (21) _____ his size.
                                              (precisely)

"My name is Herbie," said the boy. "I live in that castle. Please be my

(22) _____ . You seem so (23) _____ , unlike the
         (confidant)                         (amiable)

others. My father is a giant, but he is (24) _____ and kind. He
                                                 (congenial)

told me to choose my friends (25) _____ ."
                                       (sensibly)

PeeWee (26) _____ and became the boy's friend.
                (beamed)

News of PeeWee's friendship with the giant's son soon (27) _____
                                                                  (diffused)

throughout the kingdom . . . and from that day on, no one ever

(28) _____ PeeWee again.
         (perturbed)

# Reading

Name _____

If you spread the peanut butter
before you get the bread,
your fingers will stick together,
and there'll be trouble ahead!

Number each set of sentences 1, 2, and 3 in the correct order.

_____ Go home to get clean clothes.

_____ Fall in a muddy puddle.

_____ Try to be cool and jump over a big, muddy puddle.


_____ Start to clean a very messy bedroom at 9:00 a.m.

_____ Go back to the bedroom to finish cleaning at 1:00 p.m.

_____ Eat a big lunch at noon.


_____ Learn a silly joke.

_____ Tell the joke to your friends.

_____ Watch your audience laugh loudly.


_____ Place the roller blades in the closet.

_____ Put on brand-new roller blades.

_____ Skate until your feet hurt.


_____ Carefully rub your sore tummy.

_____ Eat the candy very quickly.

_____ Buy lots of yummy candy at the store.


_____ Swing the bat carefully.

_____ Walk to home plate with a bat.

_____ Hit the ball hard and run.

# Reading

Name _____

A weatherman prepares ahead,
and you can do this, too.
Just study very carefully
each and every clue.

Decide what will happen next by underlining the sentence that would best complete each cartoon strip. Then draw a picture to show that sentence.

a. Magician pulls a rabbit from his hat.
b. Magician puts the hat on his head.

a. The children go ice skating at the park.
b. The children put a hat on the snowman's head.

a. The organ grinder slips on a banana peel.
b. The organ grinder begins to sing.

13

# Reading

Name _____

Can you always
    believe what you read,
or does information
    sometimes mislead?

Read each newspaper article. Then circle the answer to each question.

## Inventor Takes Flight

"You'll feel lighter than air!" ex-claimed Dr. I.M. Uphigh.

The well-known inventor recently created a special shoe. Its secret lies in the soles. Hundreds of little rubber balls are placed tightly inside the rubber soles. Whenever a person feels like flying, he just bounces on his feet and up he goes! "You'll have a ball!" Uphigh told the surprised reporters.

1. What is Dr. Uphigh's occupation?
   a. dentist    b. pilot    c. inventor

2. What makes his shoes special?
   a. rubber soles    b. rubber balls
   c. bright lights

3. Where would his invention work best?
   a. on cement    b. in mud
   c. in a lake

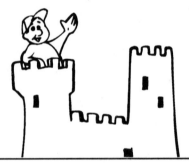

1. What was special about Mr. Shore?
   a. He was king of a sand castle
   b. He was mayor.
   c. He built sand castles

2. How long did he live in his castle?
   a. 8 days    b. 38 days    c. 83 days

3. What happened to the castle?
   a. Rain destroyed it.
   b. The mayor bought it.
   c. Mr. Shore moved it to a new
      place.

## Our City's Own Sandman

Mr. C. Shore has won a bet with our mayor. He proved that a man's castle is his home. For 83 days he lived on the beach in his own castle made from wet sand. During his stay, Mr. Shore said, "I feel like a king."

Mr. Shore's reign finally ended when a huge rainstorm invaded his kingdom, and his castle by the sea quickly disappeared.

# Reading

Name _____

Old Farmer McFarkle
had a farm
where inventions he made
which worked like a charm.

Read about Farmer McFarkle's farm. Circle the letter that states the main idea of each paragraph.

1. Farmer McFarkle built a very modern barn. Inside the barn he put a food machine for the animals. When they were hungry, the animals pushed a button and out popped fruit, vegetables, or hay. The clever farmer even installed speakers so that the animals could listen to "Old McFarkle Had a Farm" or "The Sound of Moosic."
   a. Speakers play music in a barn.
   b. McFarkle built a modern barn.
   c. The animals ate healthy farm food.

2. Cowabunga Cow gave the McFarkle family lots of milk every day. Her milk was wonderful because it came in different flavors—vanilla, chocolate, and strawberry. On cold days she even gave Neapolitan ice cream!
   a. Cowabunga was a cow that loved milk.
   b. Cowabunga was a white, brown, and pink cow.
   c. Cowabunga was a cow that made special milk.

3. Farmer McFarkle, tired of the eggs falling from the nests and cracking on the floor, had his hens sit on boxes instead of nests. After awhile, the hens began to lay square eggs that didn't roll.
   a. McFarkle solved a problem.
   b. McFarkle had square hens.
   c. McFarkle ate eggs for breakfast.

4. The pigs on the McFarkle farm loved to roll in the mud. Farmer McFarkle didn't want to spoil their fun, but he did want his farm to be clean and tidy. So he built a pig shower. When pigs stepped onto a rolling belt, it moved them toward the shower where they were sprayed clean.
   a. The pigs enjoyed rolling in the mud.
   b. The pigs ate too much.
   c. McFarkle discovered a way to clean dirty pigs.

# English

Name _____

**Tongue Twister**

(Say it quickly)

The wonderful old woman washed windows on Wednesday while her children chose chores of their choice.

The children decided to help the old woman organize some things in the crowded shoe by putting them in ABC order. Help them by numbering each group of words.

### Pantry

_____ flour     _____ pretzels

_____ soup     _____ crackers

_____ syrup     _____ candy

_____ cocoa     _____ popcorn

### Kitchen Cupboard

_____ pots

_____ pans

_____ bowls

_____ plates

### Refrigerator

_____ milk     _____ bacon

_____ juice     _____ beef

_____ soda     _____ hamburger

_____ cream     _____ ham

### Toy Chest

_____ dolls

_____ trucks

_____ games

_____ balls

### Closet

_____ sweaters     _____ slippers

_____ shirts     _____ loafers

_____ jackets     _____ sandals

_____ pants     _____ tennis shoes

### Bedroom

_____ blanket

_____ bedspread

_____ pillow

_____ sheets

# English

Name _____

**Tongue Twister**
Sophia Spooner spoke so speedily
that she worded the words all wrong.

Read what Sophia said about her trip to the circus. Put the words in correct sentence order. Add capitals and punctuation.

1. growled tamer lions the loudly the at

   _____

2. toes their danced dogs on the

   _____

3. an lady trunk elephant lifted with a its

   _____

4. artists trapeze the air in swung high

   _____

5. pretzel man body twisted his like a one

   _____

6. ate candy cotton pink children

   _____

7. a stilts wooden clown walked on

   _____

8. around horses ten ran the ring

   _____

# English

Name _____

**Tongue Twister**
Cindy Sue selected cereal that provided
proper prizes with proper proof of purchase.

Discover what toy prizes Cindy chose by writing the letter that comes **before** each letter below. The prizes are all nouns which name people, places, or things.

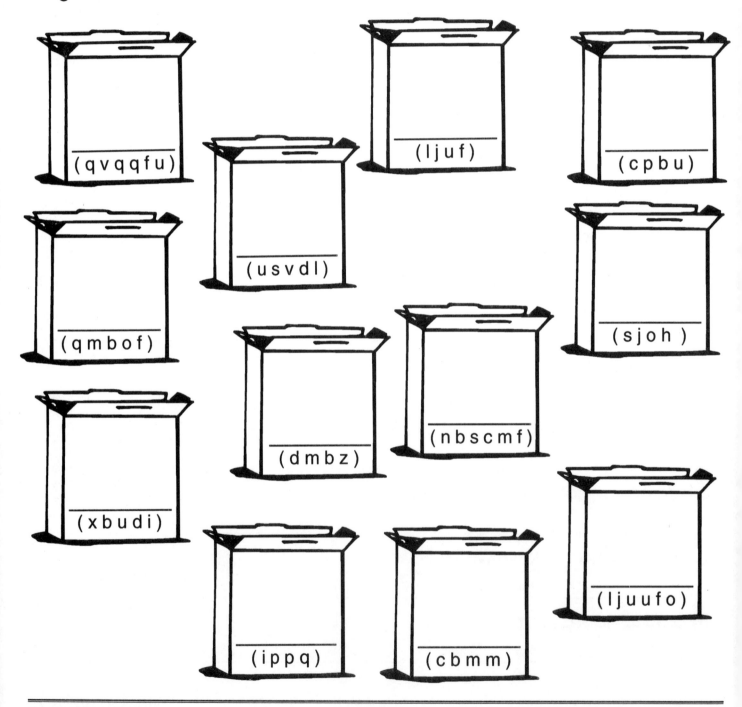

( q v q q f u )

( l j u f )

( c p b u )

( u s v d l )

( q m b o f )

( s j o h )

( d m b z )

( n b s c m f )

( x b u d i )

( i p p q )

( c b m m )

( l j u u f o )

# English

**Tongue Twister**
Directors direct drama dramatically.

Ms. Dee Rector is directing ten movies. She always seems to be yelling, "Action!" Underline each action verb. Then write a new verb to make each sentence silly.

1. T.R. Zan swung quickly on the tree's long vines. _____

2. Miss May Kup winked sweetly at the movie's hero, Mr. I. Scott Muscles.

    _____

3. Otto B. Astar escaped the wild and angry elephants. _____

4. Willie Makeit carefully climbed up the side of the towering skyscraper.

    _____

5. Miss Lotta Charm swayed to the beat of the loud music. _____

6. Mr. Kenny D. Zine drew the blueprints for a bridge between the two

    continents. _____

7. Cara Lot kissed the little, lost puppy on his cold nose. _____

8. Jimmy A. Locke opened the large bank vault. _____

9. Barry M. Azing, with his super powers, lifted the erupting volcano from the

    ground. _____

10. Lief Mia Lone built a huge castle in the middle of an island. _____

# English

Name _____

**Tongue Twister**
Reflections reveal realistic reproductions.

Mirrors are like copy machines. Write the plural for each noun. Then draw each reflection in the mirror.

elf _____

fox _____

cherry _____

mouse _____

watch _____

leaf _____

lady _____

child _____

ball _____

bunny _____

tooth _____

box _____

IF8784 Second Grade in Review

# English

Name _____

## Tongue Twister
**Quiz your acquaintances with
quick, inquiring questions.**

Someone's been asking Mother Goose some questions, and she's been telling
some secrets. Add a period to each statement and a question mark to each
question. Then, write the letter of each statement or question next to its
matching sentence.

____  He spilled ink all over himself

____  Why did Humpty Dumpty fall

____  A fly had flown into her bowl

____  Why was Mary quite contrary

____  Where were Little Bo Peep's
sheep

____  The clock struck one

____  Why did London Bridge fall
down

____  Why did Little Jack Horner sit in
the corner

a.  Why did the spider sit by Little
Miss Muffet

b.  Someone greased the wall

c.  The bunnies had eaten her
flowers

d.  He ate too many of his mother's
pies

e.  Its braces needed tightening

f.  They were selling their wool at
the market

g.  Why was Little Boy blue

h.  Why did the mouse run down the
clock

# English

Name _____

**Tongue Twister**
Sherlock shadowed the shadow of the shifty,
shameless, short, sharp-nosed shoplifter.

Sherlock always looked for the true meaning of each clue so he would not
make a mistake. Find the incorrect meaning of each word and underline it.

1. hard
   a. not soft
   b. shiny
   c. difficult

2. pet
   a. tame animal
   b. pat gently
   c. a deep hole

3. seal
   a. a type of boat
   b. a sea mammal
   c. to close completely

4. file
   a. tool used for grinding
   b. to arrange papers in order
   c. to take up a whole space

5. star
   a. a distant sun
   b. to look at steadily
   c. actor in leading role

6. fly
   a. an insect
   b. move through the air
   c. an instrument

7. dough
   a. to dig a hole
   b. slang for money
   c. mixture of flour and water

8. right
   a. opposite of left
   b. to use a pencil
   c. correct

9. basket
   a. score made by tossing a ball through a net
   b. a container
   c. part of a wall

10. down
    a. opposite of up
    b. soft feathers
    c. pile of sand

11. ball
    a. metal object that rings
    b. a round object
    c. a formal dance

12. cool
    a. a little cold
    b. a fuel
    c. calm

# English

Name _____

**Tongue Twister**
The shoes on the shelves have similar shapes,
but the shoes on the dock are different.

**Synonyms** have similar meanings. **Antonyms** are opposites. Write a synonym for each word in a shoe on a shelf. Write an antonym for each word in a shoe on a dock. Use the Word Bank.

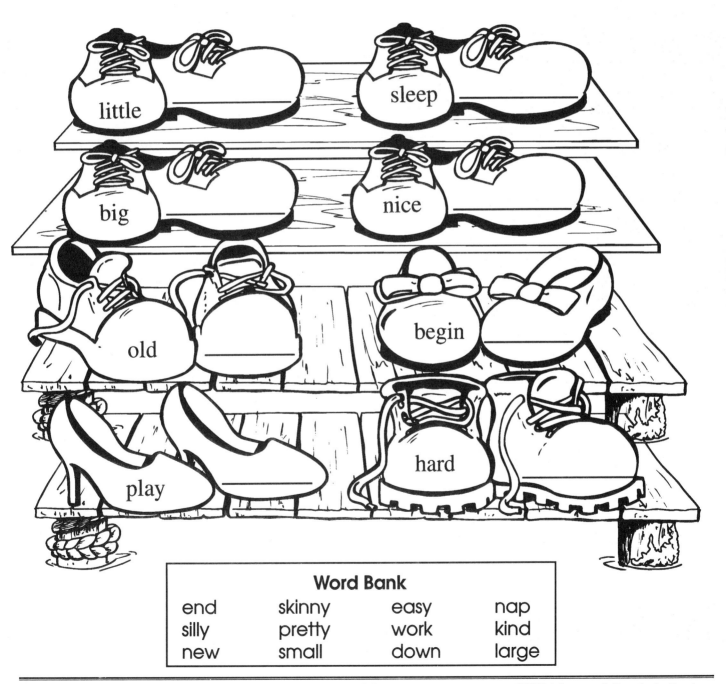

little _____     sleep _____

big _____     nice _____

old _____     begin _____

play _____     hard _____

| Word Bank | | | |
|---|---|---|---|
| end | skinny | easy | nap |
| silly | pretty | work | kind |
| new | small | down | large |

# English

Name _____

**Tongue Twister**
Tennessee tightly tensed up the
tension on his tennis racket.

Verb tense tells when an action occurs: in the past, at the present time, or in the future. Write the correct verb for each sentence.

1. At yesterday's match the boxer _____ himself to be a real dog.
   (prove, proved, proving)

2. The baseball player _____ to jail because he stole a base.
   (go, went, going)

3. The golfer is _____ his pants because he got a hole in one.
   (change, changed, changing)

4. The football players _____ cool because they have many fans.
   (stay, stayed, staying)

5. The only thing the fisherman _____ was a cold.
   (catches, caught, catching)

6. The waitress is _____ about becoming a tennis player
   (think, thought, thinking)
   because she serves so well.

7. The deep sea diver _____ peanut butter in case he
   (brings, brought, bringing)
   catches a jellyfish.

8. The fisherman _____ not to clean the fish because
   (decide, decided, deciding)
   it had been in water all day.

9. The runner is fast because he _____ athlete's foot.
   (has, had, having)

10. The basketball player _____ to help the Easter
    (promise, promised, promising)
    Bunny because he stuffs baskets so well.

# English

Name _____

**Tongue Twister**
Owen owned the only oboe in Ohio.

A noun can show ownership by adding **'s** or **s'**. If the noun is singular, add **'s**. If the noun is plural, add **s'**. Add apostrophes in the sentences where needed.

1. Can a pianos key open anything?

2. Tims tuba would be lighter if it were a *one-ba.*

3. Does a fishs scale sound better than a singers scale?

4. The conductors watch keeps time to the music.

5. The orchestras favorite dessert is *cello.*

6. Some musicians teeth sparkle because they use a *tuba* toothpaste.

7. The violins bow makes it more present-able.

8. A rubber bands music has lots of snap!

9. Does a baseball players pitch help him sing better?

10. That musicians favorite Christmas treat is *flute-cake.*

# Spelling

Name _____

Clementine Clown loves to dress in very silly clothing. Fill in the blanks with the missing short vowels to spell what she is wearing.

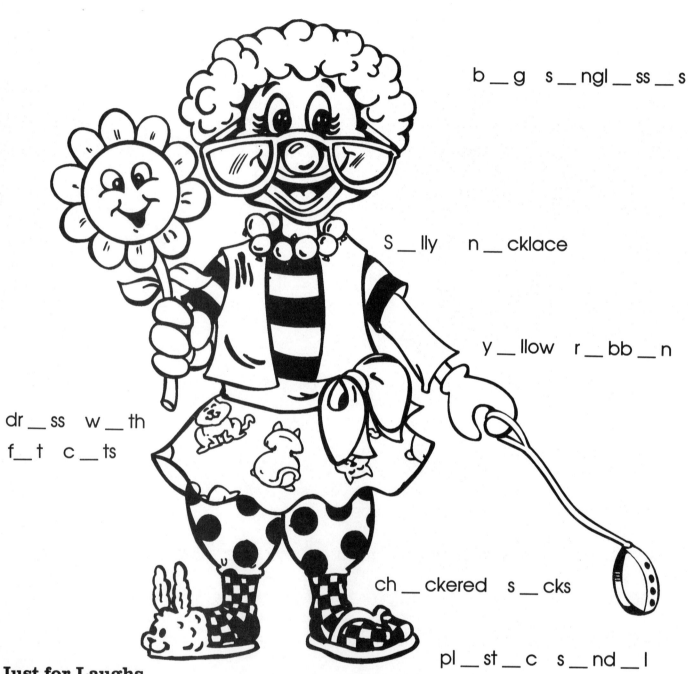

b __ g   s __ ngl __ ss __ s

s __ lly   n __ cklace

y __ llow   r __ bb __ n

dr __ ss   w __ th
f __ t   c __ ts

ch __ ckered   s __ cks

pl __ st __ c   s __ nd __ l

**Just for Laughs**

Why d __ d Cl __ ncy y __ ll wh __ n Cl __ m __ ntine pr __ ssed
h __ s p __ nts?

*Because he was st __ ll __ n th __ m!*

26   IF8784 Second Grade in Review

# Spelling

Name _____

See what Sadie ate by unscrambling the letters to write words with long vowel sounds.

**Just for Laughs**

How did S __ die f __ el after sh __ swallowed her __ wn t __ il?

*L __ ke sh __ was g __ ing around in circles.*

# Spelling

Name _____

Write the missing consonant blends and you will see what the Trash Monster gave each of his friends.

| br | cl | dr | fr | gr | pr | sn | spr | str |
|----|----|----|----|----|-----|----|-----|-----|
| bl | cr | fl | gl | pl | scr | sp | st | tr |

**Humpty Dumpty**

_ _ ue

_ _ aster

first-aid _ _ eam

safety _ _ _ ap

**Little Miss Muffet**

_ _ ool

_ _ oon

_ _ eam

_ _ ider   _ _ _ ay

**Cinderella**

_ _ oom

_ _ ippers

_ _ ock

_ _ own

_ _ ince

**Old Mother Hubbard**

_ _ ead

_ _ ackers

_ _ uitcake

_ _ ankfurters

_ _ ew

**Three Little Pigs**

_ _ _ aw

_ _ icks

_ _ icks

_ _ eel

_ _ anite

**Mary, Mary Quite Contrary**

_ _ owers

_ _ ants

_ _ ossoms

**Frog Prince**

_ _ icket

_ _ agonflies

_ _ ies

**Just for Laughs**

Why did the _ _ ash Monster _ _ and outside the furniture _ _ ant?

*He was _ _ ooping for table _ _ _ _ aps!*

# Spelling

Name _____

Write the final consonant blend for each word. Color each toe by blending the colors shown on Ernest's Color Chart.

### Ernest's Color Chart

| | | |
|---|---|---|
| **ft** = blue/red | **nd** = yellow/brown | **nt** = yellow/red |
| **lt** = purple/red | **nk** = yellow/green | **pt** = orange/red |
| **mp** = pink/orange | **ld** = purple/brown | **st** = black/red |

CHE _ _   QUI _ _   HA _ _

SPLI _ _   TRA _ _   SHI _ _

BLO _ _   SLE _ _   YA _ _

PAI _ _   HAU _ _ _   THE _ _

TWI _ _   BRA _ _   SLA _ _

FAI _ _   CHI _ _   FA _ _

**Just for Laughs**

Where did Erne _ _   ho _ _ _   his gra _ _ opening?

*In a toe truck*

# Spelling

Name _____

Use the clues to write the correct double consonant (**ff**, **ss**, **ll**, or **zz**) at the end of each word.

1. che __ __ = a game

2. hi __ __ = a small mountain

3. le __ __ = not more

4. pu __ __ = small cloud of smoke

5. hi __ __ = snake noise

6. cu __ __ = bottom of sleeve

7. fi __ __ = bubbles in a drink

8. se __ __ = opposite of buy

9. fu __ __ = lint on sweater

10. gu __ __ = a sea bird

11. ra __ __ = to tease

12. me __ __ = clutter

13. ye __ __ = to scream

14. gla __ __ = holds a drink

15. du __ __ = not sharp

16. sni __ __ = to smell

17. we __ __ = not sick

18. bu __ __ = bee's sound

19. pi __ __ = tablet

20. dre __ __ = gown

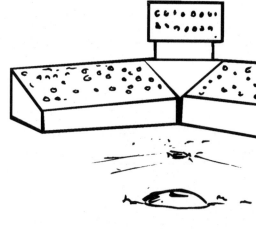

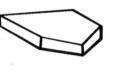

**Just for Laughs**

What do you ca __ __ twins who walk acro __ __ the baseba __ __ diamond stu __ __ ed inside the same shirt? *A double-header*

# Spelling

Name _____

Add a word to make a **compound word** with both the word on the left and the word on the right. Then complete the riddle by writing the boxed letters in the correct blanks.

**Word Bank**

| | | | |
|---|---|---|---|
| ground | room | watch | cup |
| wheel | ball | drop | fire |
| suit | moon | sand | fly |
| yard | neck | paper | book |

wrist ___ [18] ___ [10] ___ dog

camp ___ [7] ___ [15] wood

foot ___ [12] ___ ___ room

pin ___ ___ [4] [9] ___ chair

rain ___ ___ ___ [17] out

fire [6] ___ ___ paper

honey ___ ___ ___ [19] light

mush [8] ___ ___ ___ mate

swim [3] [1] ___ [5] case

under ___ [11] ___ ___ ___ ___ hog

quick [24] ___ ___ ___ man

turtle ___ ___ [20] [22] lace

note ___ ___ ___ [14] worm

sand [2] ___ ___ [23] ___ boy

back ___ [21] [16] ___ stick

butter [13] ___ ___ cake

**Just for Laughs**

Why did the ___ ___ ___ ___ ___ man put a
　　　　　　　　1　2　3　4　5

___ ___ ___ ___ _C_ ___ ___ ___ ___ ___ ___
6　7　8　9　10　11　12　13　14　15　16

under his ___ _A_ ___ ___ ___ ___ ___ ___ ?
　　　　17　18　19　20　21　22　23　24

*He wanted to blow his stack!*

# Spelling

Name _____

Write the contraction for each pair of cars.

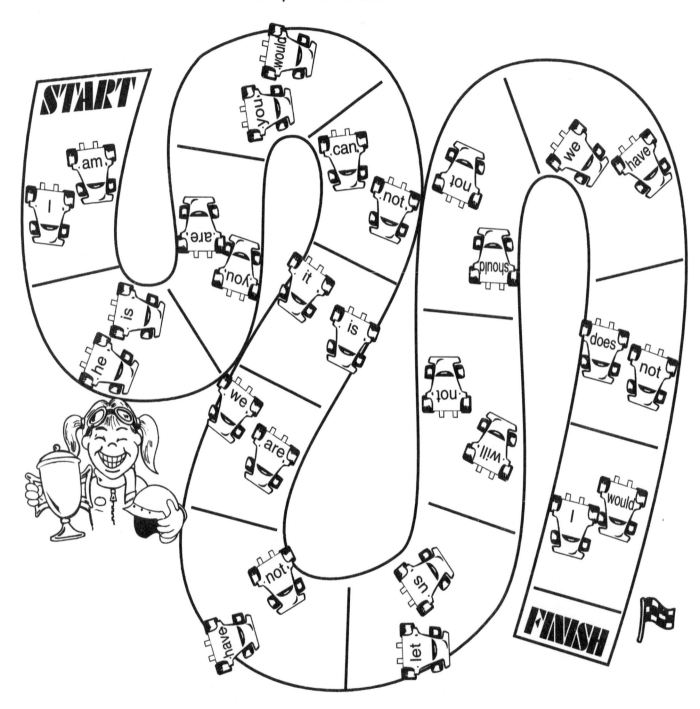

**Just for Laughs**

What did one muffler say to the other after the long race?

_____ *exhausted!* _____ *you?*
      (I am)                    (Are not)

# Spelling

Name _____

Shhhh! Write the silent letter (**b, g, k, t,** or **w**) missing from each word.

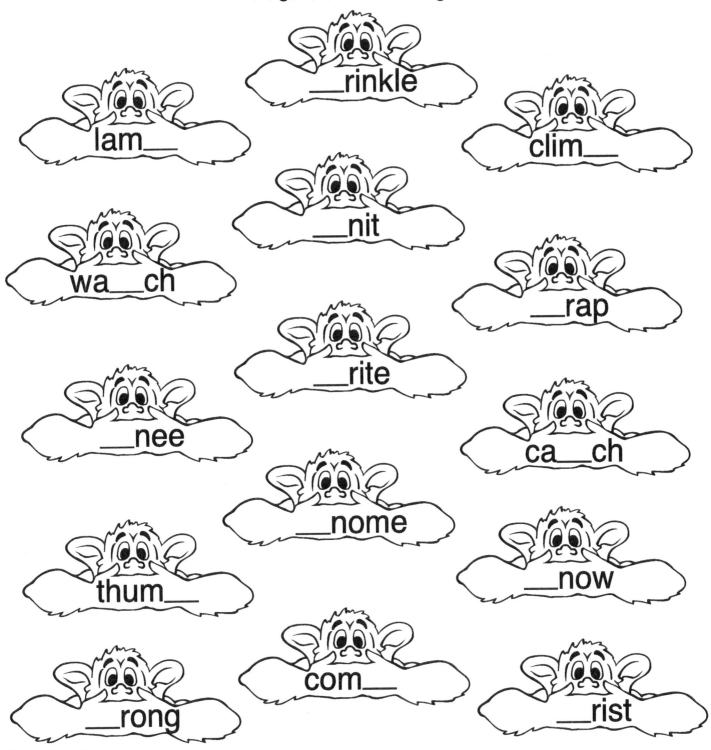

lam__

__rinkle

clim__

__nit

wa__ch

__rap

__nee

__rite

ca__ch

thum__

__nome

__now

__rong

com__

__rist

**Just for Laughs**

How did the reporter __ now where the monkey clim __ ed?

*He wa __ ched the monkey and dictated his findings into an ape recorder.*

# Spelling

Name _____

Listen carefully! Unscramble the scrambled homophone and write it on the line.

hare – rhai _____

wood – wlduo _____

wear – eerhw _____

male – lmai _____

write – trhgi _____

ant – utna _____

ate – htieg _____

cent – nsect _____

sum – seom _____

blue – lwbe _____

rays – seair _____

pear – iarp _____

**Just for Laughs**

What may happen if you call a _____ family on _____
telephone?

(ebe)                                    (trehi)

_____ may _____ a buzzy signal.

(htree)         (eb)

# Spelling

Name _____

Read each story ending. Use the Word Bank to add a suffix to the end of each base word and write the new word on the line.

**Word Bank**

| | | |
|---|---|---|
| ness | est | s |
| ed | er | ful |

1. . . . and the _____ boy of all went to live in the castle.
(poor)

2. . . . and the little elf _____ into the thick forest.
(disappear)

3. . . . and the clever mouse _____ himself to be _____
(prove) (smart)
than the huge lion.

4. . . . and the baby elephant finally _____ to his mother.
(return)

5. . . . and the _____ of the old woman _____ their
(kind) (fill)
hearts with joy.

6. . . . and the _____ frog _____ _____
(surprise) (jump) (high)

than all of the _____ and was never seen again.
(cloud)

7. . . . and the lazy dragon became the _____ creature in the
(fat)
kingdom.

8. . . . and the wise king _____ to share his gold with the poor
(continue)
people.

**Just for Laughs**

How can you tell that many clock _____ _____ fairy tales?
(maker) (invent)

*Each story _____ with "Once upon a time . . . "*
(begin)

# Spelling

Name _____

Complete each riddle by writing a day of the week in the blank.

**Word Bank**

| Friday | Thursday | Saturday |
| Sunday | Wednesday | Tuesday |
| Monday | | |

1. I'm two days before the first day of the weekend.

   I am _____ .

2. I come in second on the calendar and in alphabetical order.

   I am _____ .

3. Although I stand in the middle of the school week, I am last when placed in alphabetical order.   I am _____ .

4. Although calendars show me as the first day of the week, many consider me the last day of the weekend.   I am _____ .

5. I may be the first day when arranged in alphabetical order, but I am the last day of school before the weekend.   I am _____ .

6. I am spaced exactly in the middle between Sunday and Thursday.

   I am _____ .

7. Depending on how you looked at it, I am either the last day of the week or the first day of the weekend.   I am _____ .

Now rewrite the days of the week in the order they are shown on a calendar.

1. _____     5. _____

2. _____     6. _____

3. _____     7. _____

4. _____

# Spelling

Name _____

Use the clues to write the name of each month.

1. _____ ril
   (a monkey minus *e*)

2. Sept _____
   (burning coal)

3. _____
   (to lift knees high while walking)

4. Aug _____ t
   (not them)

5. Dec _____
   (member minus the first *m*)

6. _____ y
   (short for Julie)

7. Oc _____ ber
   (part of foot minus *e*)

8. _____ uary
   (nickname for Janice)

9. _____
   (rhymes with tune)

10. _____ ruary
    (rhymes with web)

11. _____ mber
    (rhymes with stove)

12. _____ l?
    (asking permission)

Write the names of the months in order.

1. _____
2. _____
3. _____
4. _____
5. _____
6. _____

7. _____
8. _____
9. _____
10. _____
11. _____
12. _____

**Just for Laughs**

What does Tarzan sing in _____ ?

*"Jungle Bells"*

# Spelling

Name _____

Color the letters that form each word's abbreviation. Then write the abbreviation on the line. Don't forget the period!

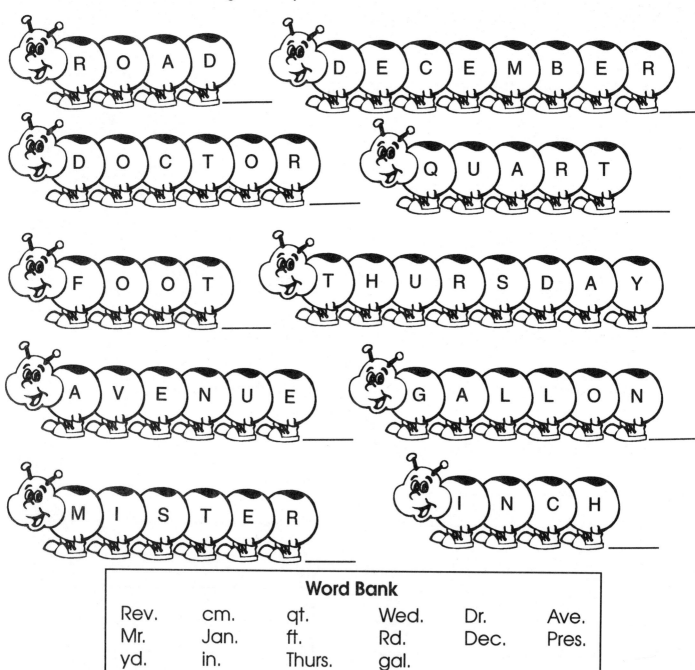

## Word Bank

| Rev. | cm. | qt. | Wed. | Dr. | Ave. |
|------|-----|-----|------|-----|------|
| Mr. | Jan. | ft. | Rd. | Dec. | Pres. |
| yd. | in. | Thurs. | gal. | | |

## Just for Laughs

Why did _____ Tom Thumb serve a centipede for Thanksgiving dinner?
(Mister)

*He wanted everyone in his family to have a drumstick.*

# Spelling

Name _____

These extraordinary spiders wear different colored socks on their unusual, long legs. Color those socks that contain a base word that can correctly join with the prefix in the spider's body to make a word.

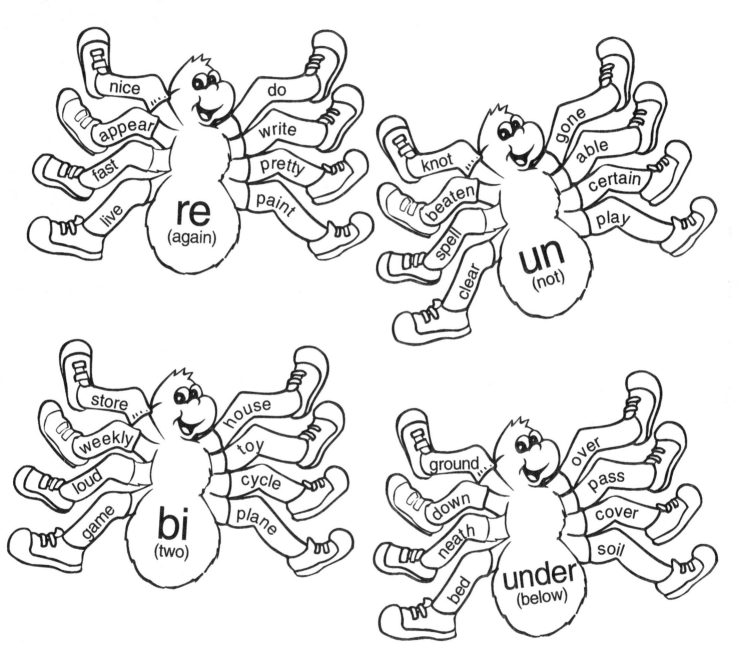

**Just for Laughs**

Why was the spider so ____ happy with his lunch?
(re, un)

*The cook had tried to ____ heat his French Flies.*
(re, un)

# Creative Writing

Name _____

You have been selected by Bowser Biscuits Dog Food to write a TV commercial advertising an exciting, new puppy food. After discussing the project with your puppy, Puddles, you know exactly what to write to convince the world that this product is best.

Write your commercial. Be sure to include the name of the product, the reason it is so special, its cost, and where it may be purchased.

_____

**Make Someone Smile**
Write a question for the riddle.

Question: _____

_____

Answer:  *Pupperoni Pizza, Muttzarella Cheese, and Pupsi Cola.*

# Creative Writing

Name _____

You have just opened a restaurant for children called **Yummies for the Tummies.** All of the food is prepared with ingredients that children love.

Create a menu. Write the name of each item and a short description. Be clever! **Example:** Frankfurterstein—a monster of a hot dog

## YUMMIES FOR THE TUMMIES
### MAIN DISHES

_____

_____

_____

_____

### SIDE ORDERS

_____

_____

_____

### DESSERTS

_____

_____

_____

### DRINKS

_____

_____

**Make Someone Smile**
Write a question for the riddle.

Question: _____

_____

**Answer:** *So that you can have your cake and eat it, too!*

# Creative Writing

Name _____

**The good news is:** You are in the world's largest toy store—Toys-R-4-U.

**The bad news is:** It is nighttime and the workers locked you inside by mistake.

## TOYS TOYS TOYS TOYS TOYS TOYS

Complete your adventure by filling in the blanks with very descriptive words.

I couldn't believe _____ . At first, I tried to

open the _____ doors, but I soon discovered that they would

be locked until _____ . So I decided that I might as well enjoy

my _____ . I walked down the _____ row and

saw a lot of _____ games. I really liked the game called

_____ because _____ . Next,

I _____ down the _____ row.

Here I was _____ to see _____ robots. They

could do almost anything—even _____ ! I kept

on _____ until I suddenly found myself standing face-to-face

with a giant _____ . I couldn't believe it when

_____ . Finally, I came to the outdoor toys

where there were many different kinds of _____.I couldn't stop

laughing because _____ . Then, I heard a

_____ noise. I realized that this _____ store was

opening. I casually walked toward the front door, looked _____

at a clerk, and said, " _____ ."

**Make Someone Smile**
Complete the joke.

**The good news is:** You've just won a $1,000 shopping spree in a toy store.

**The bad news is:** _____

# Creative Writing

Name _____

You are the manager of Percival's Peculiar Pet Shop. The pets are so unusual that it is necessary to give extra information about each one. So that you don't have to keep repeating yourself, you've decided to place a sign near each pet.

Make a sign for four of the most peculiar animals. Include the type of animal, its name, where it was born, and what traits make it so unusual.

**Make Someone Smile**

Write an answer for the riddle.

**Question:** What do you get when you cross a crocodile with a gorilla?

Answer: _____

# Creative Writing

Name _____

You are an editor of a large book company. Your job is to create snappy titles for new books.

Read the short summary for each book. Then write titles that will get the shoppers' attention so that they will want to buy each one.

_____

For many years, Dr. Iva Lightfoot worked very hard to develop an antigravity formula. On the day that she finally was successful, her dog unknowingly drank the mixture.

_____

Minnie, a tiny seven-year-old, visited a rocket launch center. She wandered away from her parents and walked into a rocket ready for lift-off. Its destination was the moon. The rocket launched with her in it!

_____

The second grade class was having recess on the school playground. Suddenly, a huge UFO landed in the middle of the baseball diamond, and out walked some very strange visitors.

**Make Someone Smile**
Carefully read the author's name. Then write a funny title for the book.

by
Belle E. Button

by
Dan D. Lion

by
Char Lee Horse

# Creative Writing

Name _____

The city zoo needs some improvements. Ms. Annie Mulluver, the manager, has asked interested people to write letters on how to improve it. You have some fantastic, new ideas. Write about them in the letter below.

Dear _____ ,

_____

_____

_____

_____

_____

_____

_____

_____

_____

_____

_____ ,

_____

**Make Someone Smile**
The animals have ideas about zoo improvements, too. Finish their statements.

I'm not *lyin'* . . .

_____

_____

_____

Don't *monkey* around.

_____

_____

_____

I can't *bear* to see

_____

_____

_____

# Creative Writing

Name _____

Choose a title. Then write a story that is out-of-this-world. Illustrate your story last.

### Titles

My Teacher, the Alien

My Summer Vacation on Mars

What the Man on the Moon Is Really Like

Learning Proper Alien Manners

The Moon's Amusement Park

_____

_____

_____

_____

_____

_____

_____

_____

_____

_____

**Make Someone Smile**

Write an answer for the riddle.

Question: How would you shake hands with a six-armed Martian?

Answer: _____

# Creative Writing

Name _____

**The Sleepyhead**

Make a cartoon strip about something funny that happened to you or to someone in your family. Name your cartoon strip in the first box. Then use the rest of the boxes to draw your cartoon.

**Remember:** To show someone talking use ...

To show someone thinking use ...

| | |
|---|---|
| 1. | 2. |
| 3. | 4. |
| 5. | 6. |
| 7. | 8. |

# Creative Writing

Name _____

Before Miss Teree writes a story, she thinks really hard about her subject. Then she lists any words that relate to the story. This is called **brainstorming**.

Read each story idea. Then list any words that relate. When you are finished use another piece of paper to write a story using one of these titles and the words you listed.

**A Dark Cave**

_____

_____

_____

_____

_____

**A Mysterious Castle**

_____

_____

_____

_____

_____

**The Lost Treasure**

_____

_____

_____

_____

_____

**A Ship on the Ocean**

_____

_____

_____

_____

_____

**Make Someone Smile**        Knock, knock.
            *Who's there?*
        Doughnut.
            *Doughnut who?*
        Doughnut bother me when I brainstorm!

# Creative Writing

Name _____

Oh, no! Suddenly you've become invisible! What caused this? What things will you do now that you are invisible? How long will this last?

First, create a title for your story. Next, brainstorm and list words and ideas that will help you write your story. Then, create an interesting tale.

_____
(title)

_____     _____     _____
_____     _____     _____
_____     _____     _____
_____     _____     _____

_____
_____
_____
_____
_____
_____
_____
_____
_____
_____
_____

**Make Someone Smile**
Write a question for the riddle:

Question: _____

Answer: *Evaporated milk and chocolate chip cookies*

© Instructional Fair, Inc.                    49                    IF8784 Second Grade in Review

# Creative Writing

Name _____

Wow!!!
You just interviewed a visitor from another
planet for the school newspaper! With your super questions
and your guest's amazing answers, you are certain to
receive the "Remarkable Reporter Award."

Write your questions and your visitor's answers on the lines below.

Question: _____

Answer: _____

Question: _____

Answer: _____

Question: _____

Answer: _____

Question: _____

Answer: _____

Question: _____

Answer: _____

## Make Someone Smile

Draw yourself and the alien in these cartoons to show part of your interview.

| What's your favorite ball game? | A double-header, of course. | Where do you go fishing? | In the "galax-seas." | Why are you so green? | I need to ripen in the sun. |
| --- | --- | --- | --- | --- | --- |
| | | | | | |

# Creative Writing

Name _____

Create a story to go with the ending sentence. Make sure that it blends smoothly into the ending.

_____

_____

_____

_____

_____

_____

_____

_____

_____

_____

_____

_____

_____

_____

_____

_____

. . . And that is the real reason that the chicken crossed the road!

**Make Someone Smile**
Write something funny that your chicken might say.

# Creative Writing

Name _____

Create an ending to this spooky tale.

One dark and creepy night my friend Tiny and I slowly walked toward the rickety, old, wooden house at the end of the block. We tiptoed up the front walk as silently as possible. Tiny gently pushed the doorbell, but nothing happened. So he reached for the rusty doorknob and carefully turned it. The huge door creaked, squeaked, and finally opened. We stepped cautiously inside, and . . .

**Make Someone Smile:** Draw/color the characters for this cartoon.

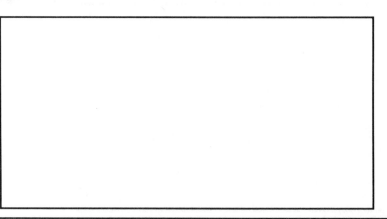

# Creative Writing

Name _____

Choose words from each list of rhyming words to help you write a short poem.
Draw a picture to go with each one.

bat, cat, chat, fat, flat, hat, pat, mat, rat, sat

_____

_____

_____

_____

bean, clean, green, keen, lean, mean, queen, scene, screen, seen

_____

_____

_____

_____

deal, eel, feel, heel, kneel, meal, peel, real, reel, seal, squeal, steal, wheel

_____

_____

_____

_____

boat, coat, float, goat, moat, note, oat, throat, vote, wrote

_____

_____

_____

_____

**Make Someone Smile:** Write a funny, rhyming poem about yourself.

_____

_____

_____

# Math

Name _____

Add the numbers in the glasses. Write the answers on the noses. Color the noses of the four largest answers.

5 + 6   9 + 8   5 + 1   9 + 7

7 + 2   3 + 3   9 + 9   2 + 9

8 + 8   4 + 5   6 + 0   3 + 4

## Calculator Calisthenics

**Question:** What was wrong with the girl who strained her eyes in the sun?

**+** the answers in each of the 4 colored noses

**x** five

**=** (Flip the calculator over.)

**Answer:** *She was _____ sick.*

# Math

Name _____

Add the number on each can of pop to the number indicated by the code.
Write the sum on the top of each can.

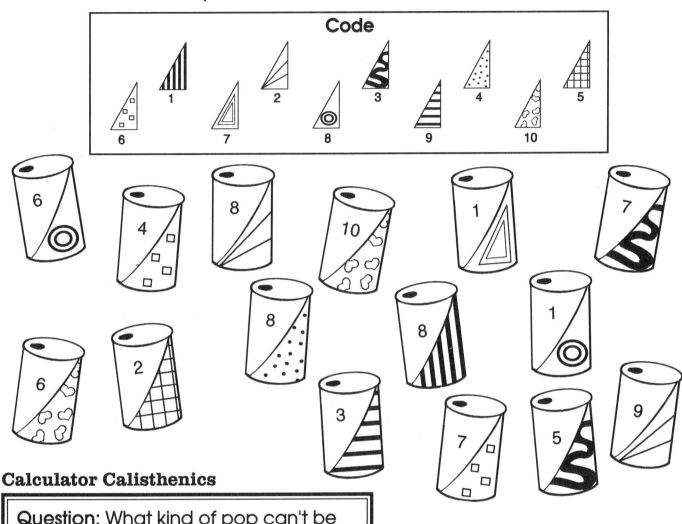

## Calculator Calisthenics

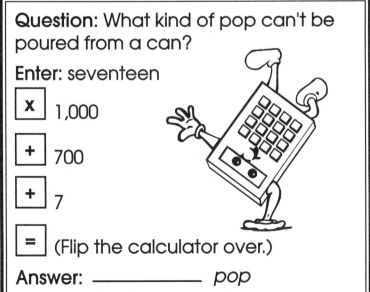

**Question:** What kind of pop can't be poured from a can?

**Enter:** seventeen

| x | 1,000 |
| + | 700 |
| + | 7 |
| = | (Flip the calculator over.) |

**Answer:** _____ *pop*

# Math

Name _____

Howdy, partner! Write the answer to each problem in the boot. In each row across, color the boots with the same answer a matching color.

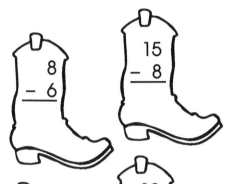

$$\begin{array}{r} 8 \\ -6 \\ \hline \end{array}$$
$$\begin{array}{r} 15 \\ -8 \\ \hline \end{array}$$
$$\begin{array}{r} 6 \\ -3 \\ \hline \end{array}$$
$$\begin{array}{r} 4 \\ -2 \\ \hline \end{array}$$
$$\begin{array}{r} 14 \\ -7 \\ \hline \end{array}$$
$$\begin{array}{r} 11 \\ -8 \\ \hline \end{array}$$

$$\begin{array}{r} 8 \\ -3 \\ \hline \end{array}$$
$$\begin{array}{r} 12 \\ -6 \\ \hline \end{array}$$
$$\begin{array}{r} 9 \\ -5 \\ \hline \end{array}$$
$$\begin{array}{r} 8 \\ -4 \\ \hline \end{array}$$
$$\begin{array}{r} 10 \\ -4 \\ \hline \end{array}$$
$$\begin{array}{r} 12 \\ -7 \\ \hline \end{array}$$

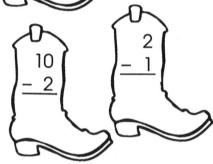

$$\begin{array}{r} 10 \\ -2 \\ \hline \end{array}$$
$$\begin{array}{r} 2 \\ -1 \\ \hline \end{array}$$
$$\begin{array}{r} 18 \\ -9 \\ \hline \end{array}$$
$$\begin{array}{r} 11 \\ -3 \\ \hline \end{array}$$
$$\begin{array}{r} 10 \\ -9 \\ \hline \end{array}$$
$$\begin{array}{r} 12 \\ -3 \\ \hline \end{array}$$

## Calculator Calisthenics

Question: What do you say to a boot with allergies?
Enter: three hundred

 309

 five

 .5378

= (Flip the calculator over.)

Answer: _____!"

IF8784 Second Grade in Review

# Math

Name _____

Make the ghosts that have problems with wrong answers disappear by crossing them out.

| $\begin{array}{r} 5 \\ -5 \\ \hline 0 \end{array}$ | $\begin{array}{r} 17 \\ -8 \\ \hline 9 \end{array}$ | $\begin{array}{r} 6 \\ -4 \\ \hline 3 \end{array}$ | $\begin{array}{r} 12 \\ -3 \\ \hline 8 \end{array}$ | $\begin{array}{r} 10 \\ -3 \\ \hline 7 \end{array}$ | $\begin{array}{r} 15 \\ -9 \\ \hline 5 \end{array}$ |

| $\begin{array}{r} 11 \\ -7 \\ \hline 3 \end{array}$ | $\begin{array}{r} 4 \\ -3 \\ \hline 1 \end{array}$ | $\begin{array}{r} 8 \\ -2 \\ \hline 6 \end{array}$ | $\begin{array}{r} 9 \\ -7 \\ \hline 1 \end{array}$ | $\begin{array}{r} 16 \\ -8 \\ \hline 8 \end{array}$ | $\begin{array}{r} 7 \\ -5 \\ \hline 2 \end{array}$ |

| $\begin{array}{r} 14 \\ -6 \\ \hline 8 \end{array}$ | $\begin{array}{r} 11 \\ -5 \\ \hline 7 \end{array}$ | $\begin{array}{r} 3 \\ -2 \\ \hline 1 \end{array}$ | $\begin{array}{r} 9 \\ -0 \\ \hline 9 \end{array}$ | $\begin{array}{r} 15 \\ -6 \\ \hline 8 \end{array}$ | $\begin{array}{r} 10 \\ -6 \\ \hline 4 \end{array}$ |

## Calculator Calisthenics

**Question:** What do you call a group of injured ghosts?

**Enter:** one thousand

[ x ] 1,000

[ x ] five

[ + ] eight thousand

[ + ] 8

[ = ] (Flip the calculator over.)

**Answer:** *A bunch of* _____

# Math

Name _____

Use the chart to help you write each problem. Then write each answer.

| Roman Numeral Chart | | | | | | | | |
|---|---|---|---|---|---|---|---|---|
| 1 | 2 | 3 | 4 | 5 | 6 | 7 | 8 | 9 |
| I | II | III | IV | V | VI | VII | VIII | IX |

**Example:**

$$
\begin{array}{r}
V = 5 \\
II = 2 \\
+ \quad IX = 9 \\
\hline
16
\end{array}
$$

III =    VI =    V =    II =    VIII =
VIII =    I =    IV =    VII =    IX =
+ IV = ___    + VII = ___    + III = ___    +VIII = ___    + II = ___

VII =    I =    VI =    IV =    IX =
III =    IX =    VII =    VII =    I =
+ IV = ___    +VIII = ___    +VIII = ___    + VI = ___    + VII = ___

VIII =    V =    VII =    VIII =    II =
IV =    IX =    II =    IX =    VI =
+ III = ___    + IV = ___    + I = ___    +VIII = ___    + V = ___

**Calculator Calisthenics**

Question: What was the Roman snake's best subject in school?

Enter: fifty-five

[ x ] 1,000

[ + ] six hundred

[ − ] 86

[ = ] (Flip the calculator over.)

Answer: _____ -tory

IF8784 Second Grade in Review

# Math

Name _____

Jack and the giant were always comparing beanstalks. The height of Jack's beanstalk is listed first on each leaf. It is followed by the height of the giant's beanstalk. Draw the correct symbol between the numbers in each pair.

| < | = | > |
|---|---|---|
| less than | equal | greater than |

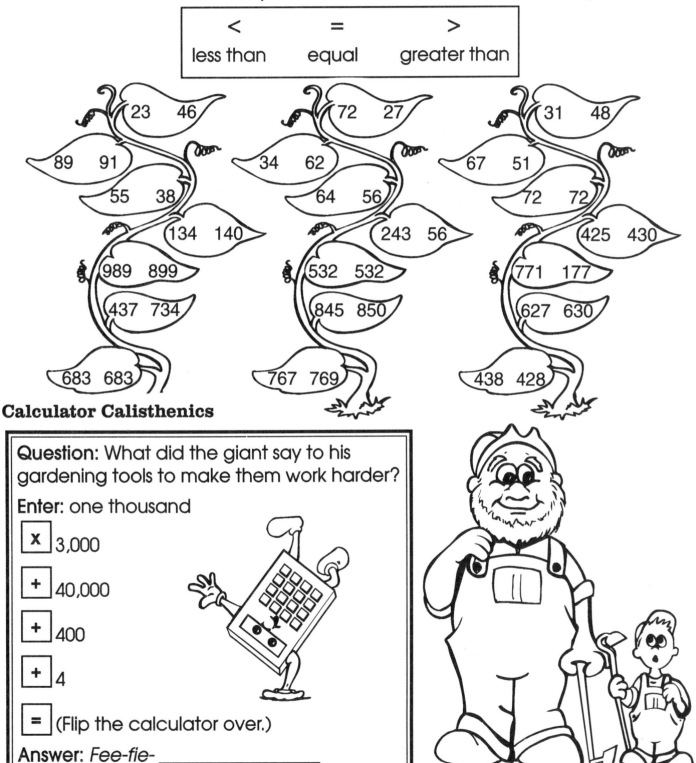

23  46      72  27      31  48

89  91      34  62      67  51

55  38      64  56      72  72

134  140    243  56     425  430

989  899    532  532    771  177

437  734    845  850    627  630

683  683    767  769    438  428

## Calculator Calisthenics

**Question:** What did the giant say to his gardening tools to make them work harder?

**Enter:** one thousand

| x | 3,000 |
| + | 40,000 |
| + | 400 |
| + | 4 |
| = | (Flip the calculator over.) |

**Answer:** *Fee-fie-* _____

# Math

Name _____

Help each fish add its two scores for the video game "Escaping Captain Hook."

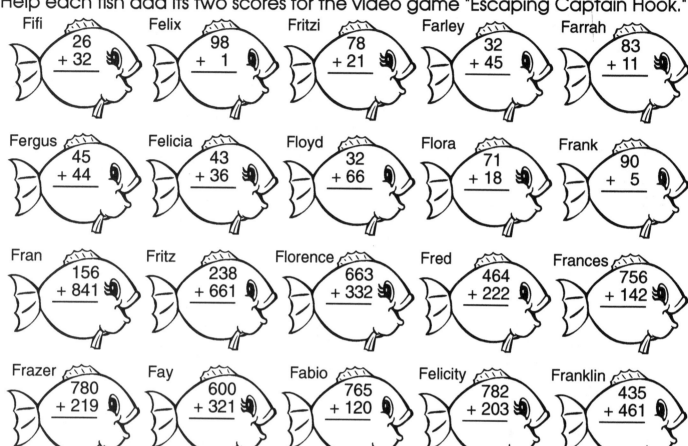

Fifi
26
+ 32

Felix
98
+ 1

Fritzi
78
+ 21

Farley
32
+ 45

Farrah
83
+ 11

Fergus
45
+ 44

Felicia
43
+ 36

Floyd
32
+ 66

Flora
71
+ 18

Frank
90
+ 5

Fran
156
+ 841

Fritz
238
+ 661

Florence
663
+ 332

Fred
464
+ 222

Frances
756
+ 142

Frazer
780
+ 219

Fay
600
+ 321

Fabio
765
+ 120

Felicity
782
+ 203

Franklin
435
+ 461

Which fish had the lowest total score? _____ ; the highest total score? _____

## Calculator Calisthenics

Question: What did the fish vote as their #1 TV show?

Enter: seven

| x | 100

| + | 50

| − | 17

| = | (Flip the calculator over.)

Answer: _____ of Fortune"

# Math

Name _____

Use the Word Bank to complete the crossword puzzle.

| Word Bank | | |
|---|---|---|
| one | four | seven |
| two | five | eight |
| three | six | nine |

**Across**

1. The number in the tens place in 549
3. $800 + 30 + 7 = 83$ _____
6. 3 ones = _____

**Down**

2. $600 + 10 + 5 = 6$ _____ 5
3. 6 hundreds = _____ 00
4. The number in the hundreds place in 873
5. 50 = _____ tens

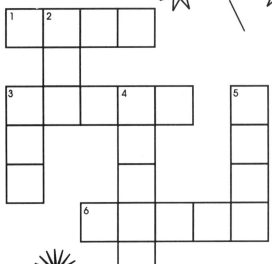

## Calculator Calisthenics

**Question:** What did the teacher say to the cross word to make it stop complaining?

**Enter:** forty-four

| x | one hundred |
| + | fifty |
| − | five |
| = | (Flip the calculator over.) |

Answer: " _____ !"

61

# Math

Name _____

Help Mortimer Mouse escape the claws of Toby Tomcat by showing him the correct path home. Add the numbers of the first problem. Then draw a line from the answer to the problem that begins with that same number. Continue adding and drawing lines until you reach Mortimer's hole. Then solve the other problems.

$$
\begin{array}{r} 24 \\ +\ 9 \\ \hline 33 \end{array}
\qquad
\begin{array}{r} 33 \\ +\ 9 \\ \hline \end{array}
\qquad
\begin{array}{r} 43 \\ +\ 37 \\ \hline \end{array}
\qquad
\begin{array}{r} 82 \\ +\ 19 \\ \hline \end{array}
$$

$$
\begin{array}{r} 24 \\ +\ 16 \\ \hline \end{array}
\qquad
\begin{array}{r} 42 \\ +\ 9 \\ \hline \end{array}
\qquad
\begin{array}{r} 51 \\ +\ 9 \\ \hline \end{array}
\qquad
\begin{array}{r} 60 \\ +\ 78 \\ \hline \end{array}
$$

$$
\begin{array}{r} 247 \\ +\ 26 \\ \hline \end{array}
\qquad
\begin{array}{r} 216 \\ +148 \\ \hline \end{array}
\qquad
\begin{array}{r} 462 \\ +129 \\ \hline \end{array}
\qquad
\begin{array}{r} 138 \\ +127 \\ \hline \end{array}
\qquad
\begin{array}{r} 208 \\ +176 \\ \hline \end{array}
$$

$$
\begin{array}{r} 326 \\ +166 \\ \hline \end{array}
\qquad
\begin{array}{r} 382 \\ +109 \\ \hline \end{array}
\qquad
\begin{array}{r} 265 \\ +127 \\ \hline \end{array}
\qquad
\begin{array}{r} 392 \\ +275 \\ \hline \end{array}
\qquad
\begin{array}{r} 627 \\ +117 \\ \hline \end{array}
$$

$$
\begin{array}{r} 482 \\ +128 \\ \hline \end{array}
\qquad
\begin{array}{r} 601 \\ +129 \\ \hline \end{array}
\qquad
\begin{array}{r} 553 \\ +168 \\ \hline \end{array}
\qquad
\begin{array}{r} 667 \\ +144 \\ \hline \end{array}
\qquad
\begin{array}{r} 811 \\ +189 \\ \hline \end{array}
$$

HOLE SWEET HOLE

## Calculator Calisthenics

**Question:** What do you get when you cross a mouse and a bulldozer?

**Enter:** one hundred

 500

 4,000

 296

= (Flip the calculator over.)

**Answer:** *Unbelievable* _____ *in your cheese.*

IF8784 Second Grade in Review

# Math

Name _____

Tucker Turtle had a big problem. He walked in his sleep—backwards! Subtract the distance he walked backwards from the distance he walked forward each day.

|  |  |  |  |  |
|---|---|---|---|---|
| **25** forward<br>**− 12** backwards<br>**13** | 46<br>− 23 | 83<br>− 40 | 78<br>− 17 | 99<br>− 25 |
| 36<br>− 21 | 64<br>− 14 | 56<br>− 11 | 80<br>− 20 | 77<br>− 14 |
| 383<br>− 252 | 768<br>− 631 | 976<br>− 852 | 387<br>− 306 | 271<br>− 131 |
| 845<br>− 432 | 662<br>− 552 | 406<br>− 101 | 592<br>− 482 | 687<br>− 616 |
| 367<br>− 255 | 546<br>− 135 | 378<br>− 251 | 989<br>− 887 | 800<br>− 200 |

## Calculator Calisthenics:

**Question:** Where did Tucker Turtle finally go for "repairs"?

**Enter:** seventy

 1,000

 7,400

 fifty-five

[=] (Flip the calculator over.)

**Answer:** _To the_ _____ _station_

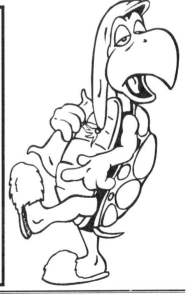

# Math

Name _____

Bloodsworth Bloodhound could sense the scent of cents so well that the U.S. Treasury Department put him in charge of counting money. How much money did he sniff in each bank? Write the answer.

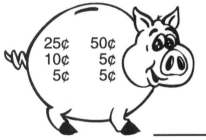
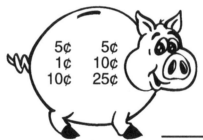

## Calculator Calisthenics

Question:
Where's the best place to keep cold cash?

Enter: seven hundred

| + | 91 |

| x | .0001 |

| = | (Flip the calculator over.) |

Answer: *In a vault in an* _____

# Math

Name _____

Every morning Grandfather Cluck wakes up Old MacDonald's family at a different time. Write each time. Then, make each clock into the face of someone in Old MacDonald's family.

_____ a.m.        _____ a.m.        _____ a.m.

_____ a.m.        _____ a.m.        _____ a.m.

_____ a.m.        _____ a.m.        _____ a.m.

## Calculator Calisthenics

**Question:** Why did Mrs. Cluck wear a watch?

**Enter:** one hundred

 41

 100

 93

= (Flip the calculator over.)

**Answer:** *So she could find _____ -tra time to read "The Little Red Hen."*

IF8784 Second Grade in Review

# Math

Name _____

Freddie Frog plays hopscotch every day, but he only hops on boxes with odd numbers. Draw an **X** on all of the boxes on which Freddie would jump.

| 5 |
|---|
| 12 | 17 |
| 62 |
| 41 |
| 59 | 72 |
| 1 |

| 4 |
|---|
| 16 | 35 |
| 83 |
| 99 |
| 30 | 57 |
| 11 |

| 9 |
|---|
| 13 | 19 |
| 28 |
| 24 |
| 38 | 69 |
| 15 |

| 2 |
|---|
| 27 | 54 |
| 39 |
| 70 |
| 43 | 92 |
| 22 |

| 65 |
|---|
| 46 | 61 |
| 735 |
| 872 |
| 454 | 701 |
| 31 |

| 86 |
|---|
| 20 | 77 |
| 665 |
| 883 |
| 989 | 888 |
| 470 |

| 24 |
|---|
| 0 | 3 |
| 288 |
| 549 |
| 677 | 53 |
| 211 |

| 51 |
|---|
| 320 | 245 |
| 446 |
| 341 |
| 756 | 558 |
| 110 |

## Calculator Calisthenics

Question: What was Freddie's job at the Lily Pad Hotel?

Enter: three hundred sixty-nine

| x | two

| + | seven thousand

| = | (Flip the calculator over.)

Answer: *He was a _____ hop.*

# Math

Name _____

The Elastic Man can bend his body in many ways. Carefully look at the diagram and use an inch ruler to draw him the correct number of inches on a large sheet of paper. Then add details to your picture for fun!

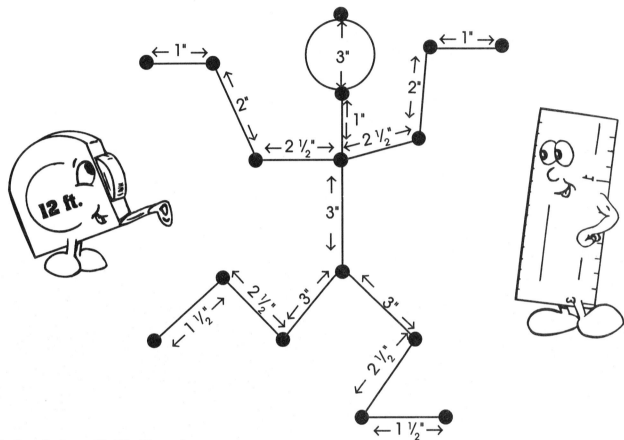

## Calculator Calisthenics

Question: What did the people name the Elastic Man after he twisted both legs to form two circles?

Enter: six hundred

| − | 91 |
| × | 100 |
| + | 37 |
| = | (Flip the calculator over.) |

Answer: _____

# Math

Name _____

Something's shaping up, and it's driving everyone buggy! First, draw a line from each geometric shape to its name.

triangle

rectangle

circle

square

octagon

cone

pyramid

cube

Now be creative and draw garden bugs using each shape.

**Calculator Calisthenics**

**Question:** What bug cannot make up its mind?

**Enter:** nine hundred

$\div$ three

$+$ fifty

$-$ twelve

$=$ (Flip the calculator over.)

**Answer:** A may-_____

# Math

Name _____

Use the Word Bank to write the missing letters of each math word.

| Word Bank | | | |
|---|---|---|---|
| ace | end | rod | rap |
| vision | sub | group | action |
| apes | cent | if | tip |

1. _____ tract
   (underwater ship)

2. g _____ h
   (kind of music)

3. di _____
   (eyesight)

4. _____ imeter
   (a penny)

5. fr _____
   (movement)

6. add _____
   (antonym of "beginning")

7. sh _____
   (monkeys)

8. p _____ uct
   (fishing pole)

9. d _____ ference
   (whether)

10. mul _____ lication
    (knock over)

11. pl _____ value
    (playing card—one)

12. re _____
    (a team)

## Calculator Calisthenics

**Question:** What letters make farm animals feel like dancing?

**Enter:** thirteen

[ + ] 1,300

[ x ] .0001

[ = ] (Flip the calculator over.)

Answer: _____

IF8784 Second Grade in Review

# Math

Name _____

Eight football teams have just completed their season. Each team played eight games. Use this pictograph to answer the questions below.

**Season Wins**  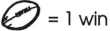 = 1 win

| | Wins |
|---|---|
| Washington Wiggle Worms | 🏈🏈🏈🏈🏈🏈🏈 |
| Kansas City Centipedes | 🏈🏈🏈🏈 |
| Pittsburgh Pandas | 🏈🏈🏈🏈🏈🏈 |
| Tampa Toucans | 🏈🏈🏈 |
| Chicago Kitty Cats | 🏈🏈🏈🏈🏈🏈🏈🏈 |
| Lansing Lightning Bugs | 🏈 |
| Houston Hornets | 🏈🏈 |
| Memphis Monkeys | 🏈 |

1. How many games did the Memphis Monkeys lose? _____

2. Which teams tied for last place? _____
   and _____

3. Which team won the season? _____

4. How many more games did the Washington Wiggle Worms win than the Tampa Toucans? _____

6. Which four teams' total number of games won equals the Chicago Kitty Cats' number of games won? _____

_____

## Calculator Calisthenics

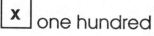

**Question:** How does a pig "pop" a football?

Enter: fifty-nine

| x | one hundred |

| + | four |

| = | (Flip the calculator over.) |

Answer: He _____ it too tightly.

# Math

Name _____

Thomas Sayva Turkey decided to offer diners new choices for Thanksgiving dinner. Chart the following choices on the bar graph. Color each bar a different color.

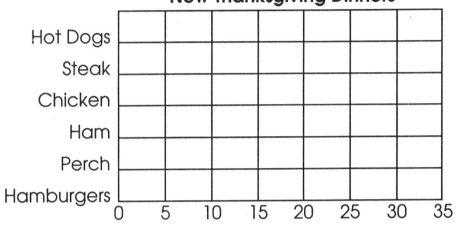

**Choices**

15 chose hamburgers
10 chose hot dogs
30 chose chicken
25 chose steak
 5 chose perch
15 chose ham

**New Thanksgiving Dinners**

Use the graph to answer the questions.

1. How many people altogether tried new Thanksgiving dinners? _____

2. Which was the favorite new meal? _____

3. Which new meal did they choose the least? _____

4. Which was a more popular choice—hamburgers or hot dogs? _____

5. How many more people chose ham than perch? _____

6. Who should be more worried now—Porky Pig or Chicken Little?

   _____

7. Which of the meals would be your first choice? _____

**Calculator Calisthenics**

Question: How can you tell when Thomas is hungry?

Enter: 5,000

| x | 1,000

| + | 378,809

| = | (Flip the calculator over.)

Answer: *By the way he _____ his food.*

# Social Studies

Name _____

Follow the directions to find the hidden treasures and surprises. Color the footsteps as you go.

## Directions

1. Begin at the pyramid. Walk 3 steps east, 1 step south, and 2 steps southeast. Draw a snake on the nearby rock to remind you to beware of the snake pit.

2. Go 2 steps directly north of the rock and 1 step east. Draw a golden necklace on this rock to show you have discovered the queen's jewelry.

3. Move 3 steps south of the jewelry. Then walk 2 steps west. Continue by going 3 steps northwest and 2 steps south. Draw a mummy on the rock. You have now found the pharoah and his queen.

4. Next, travel 2 steps northwest and 2 steps north. You are now back to the pyramid.

## Be Adventurous

Use chalk to trace your feet in all different directions on the sidewalk or driveway. Give a friend a compass and tell him which directions to follow.

# Social Studies

Name _____

Complete the pirate's treasure map by following the directions and using these symbols:

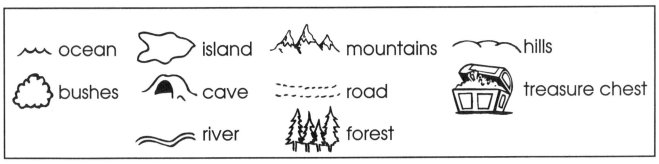

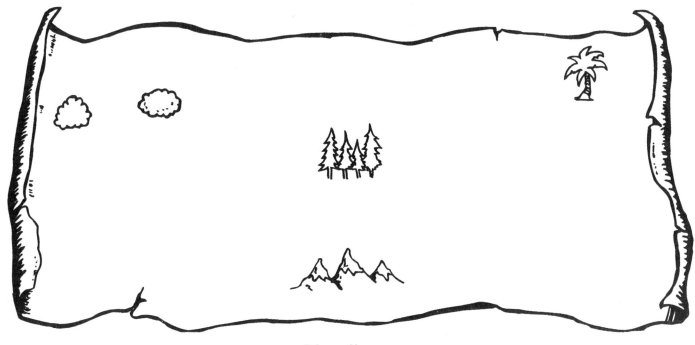

## Directions

1. Draw a cave between the bushes.
2. Draw three hills directly south of the cave.
3. Draw a road running SE from the hills to the mountains.
4. Create a river that runs north from the mountains to the forest.
5. Move NE from the forest and draw an island around the palm tree.
6. Draw a treasure chest on the far east side of the island.
7. Put an **X** on the treasure chest.

### Be Adventurous

Hide gold-covered chocolate coins or another "treasure." Then create a treasure map with directions for other students to follow to find the treasure.

# Social Studies

Name _____

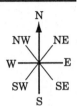

Use the clues to label the rooms on the castle's blueprints by writing the number of each room in the proper area.

### 1st Floor

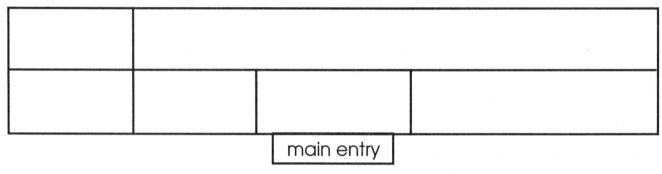

main entry

### 2nd Floor

### Clues

A. The Dining Room (1) is the longest room on the 1st floor.
B. The main entry opens into the Throne Room (2).
C. The King's Bedchamber (3) and the Queen's Bedchamber (4) are in the center of the 2nd floor with the king's room east of the queen's.
D. The Prince's Bedchamber (5) and the Princess's Bedchamber (6) are on the NW side of the 2nd floor, but the princess sleeps closer to the queen.
E. The King's Study (7) is directly west of the Throne Room.
F. The Knights' Round Table Room (8) is directly east of the Throne Room.
G. The Children's Playroom (9) is south of their bedchambers.
H. The Treasure Room (10) is on the 2nd floor.
I. The Kitchen (11) is west of the Dining Room.
J. The Servants' Quarters (12) are south of the Kitchen.

**Be Adventurous**
Build a castle using boxes and cardboard.

# Social Studies

Name _____

Use the clues to complete the names of the world's continents and oceans.

**Across:**

2. thick string or twine
3. leave it _____ is
5. opposite of in
7. a banana, ___ apple
8. another name for dad
9. a Native American

**Down:**

1. opposite of south
4. not them, but _____
6. a hardworking insect

**Be Adventurous**

Locate the continents and oceans on a world map. If possible, use a marker to draw them on an old playground ball.

75   IF8784 Second Grade in Review

# Social Studies

Name _____

The United States has many interesting places to visit. Circle the names of a few hidden below. Look → or ↓ .

## Word Bank

Liberty Bell
Lincoln Memorial
Alamo
Disney World

Yellowstone National Park
Statue of Liberty
Cape Canaveral
U.S.S. Arizona Memorial

Hollywood
White House
Mount Rushmore
Grand Canyon

**Be Adventurous**
Look at a U.S. map and find where these special places are located.

© Instructional Fair, Inc.

76

IF8784 Second Grade in Review

# Social Studies

Name _____

Every worker needs specific things to help him do his job well. After each career are listed different things which that worker may need. Put an **X** on the one that's incorrect. Then, write something which that worker might need that rhymes with the word you crossed out.

| | | | | |
|---|---|---|---|---|
| 1. **teacher**— | cook | yardstick | chalk | _____ |
| 2. **dentist**— | crown | toothbrush | gill | _____ |
| 3. **cook**— | pots | pans | grove | _____ |
| 4. **carpenter**— | hammer | claws | nails | _____ |
| 5. **artist**— | paint | mush | canvas | _____ |
| 6. **actor**— | cage | costumes | makeup | _____ |
| 7. **astronaut**— | socket | helmet | suit | _____ |
| 8. **farmer**— | tractor | barn | beads | _____ |
| 9. **writer**— | hen | paper | typewriter | _____ |
| 10. **florist**— | plants | shower | soil | _____ |

## Be Adventurous

Instead of playing "school," play "law office," "White House," "farm," or "hospital."

# Social Studies

Name _____

Unscramble the names of the holidays in the following months.

**January**
ewN reYas' yaD

_____

**February**
enalVtnie's aDy

_____

**March**
tS. rc'skitaP ayD

_____

**April**
plriA oloFs' Dya

_____

**May**
oilaMmer ayD

_____

**June**
glaF yDa

_____

**July**
delnecnepned Dya

_____

**August**

**September**
broLa aDy

_____

**October**
llowneHae

_____

**November**
ggviinksnahT

_____

**December**
stirmsaCh

_____

**Be Adventurous**
See how many other holidays you can list for each month.

# Social Studies

Name _____

Write the name of each famous American by the statement he/she may have said as a child.

| | |
|---|---|
| Benjamin Franklin | George Washington |
| Harriet Tubman | Susan B. Anthony |
| Wright Brothers | Abraham Lincoln |
| Betsy Ross | George Washington Carver |
| Thomas Edison | Alexander Graham Bell |

1. "The penny is so shiny that I can see my face in it."

   _____

2. "I can't wait to take sewing lessons!" _____

3. "I have a bright idea!" _____

4. "Hello. Hello." _____

5. "I work for peanuts." _____

6. "When I grow up, I want to be president!" _____

7. "Look! If a bird can . . . . " _____

8. "Let's all take a vote." _____

9. "All creatures and mankind need to be free!" _____

10. "I'm really shocked!" _____

**Be Adventurous**
Play Charades with your friends and take turns portraying famous Americans.

# Social Studies

Name _____

Look closely at each set of pictures. Number them in order.

**Be Adventurous**
Make cookies. Set up a stand and sell them. Use the money to buy something for your classroom.

# Social Studies

Name _____

Everyone has **needs** such as shelter, clothing, food, and love. We also have **wants**, which are things we would like to have but don't really need.

Cut out the puzzle pieces. When you put them together correctly you will have two puzzles. One will show **needs** and the other **wants**.

## Be Adventurous

Make two lists of the things in your bedroom. One list will name things you needed and the other will list things you wanted. Which is bigger?

# Social Studies

Name _____

Do you know the names of important leaders and places in your city, state, and country? If not, ask an adult to help you fill in the blanks. For every correct answer, color one space up the flagpole. See if you can reach the top!

## What is . . .

1. the name of your city or town? _____

2. the name of your state? _____

3. the name of your state's capital? _____

4. the name of your country? _____

5. the name of your country's capital? _____

## Who is (are) . . .

1. the President of the United States? _____

2. the Vice President of the United States? _____

3. your city's mayor? _____

4. your state's governor? _____

5. your state's senators? _____

6. your state's representatives? _____

## Be Adventurous

Pretend that you are the President of the United States. Write a speech that tells how you will improve your country.

# Science

Name _____

Write the answer to each riddle.

1. I protect both you and seeds from bad weather.

   What am I? _____

2. I hold hair in your head and a plant in the ground.

   What am I? _____

3. A plant cannot survive without me, but you need protection from me.

   What am I? _____

4. Both a camel and a cactus can store me for a long time.

   What am I? _____

5. I'm a gas that is helpful to plants, but I can't be bought at a gas station.

   What am I? _____

6. Many plants display my colors proudly.

   What am I? _____

7. When I grow up, the plant gets taller.

   What am I? _____

8. I may change colors, but I am not a chameleon.

   What am I? _____

9. I'm always green but not with envy.

   What am I? _____

| Word Bank | | |
| --- | --- | --- |
| stem | flower | coat |
| root | sun | chlorophyll |
| water | leaf | carbon dioxide |

**Be Curious**

Use a knife to split the stem of a white carnation about 4 or 5 inches up. Carefully place the sections in separate containers filled with different colors of food dye. Check the flower the next day. What happened? Why?

# Science

Name _____

**Endangered** animals may soon disappear from earth. That's what happened to dinosaurs, dodo birds, and passenger pigeons. They became **extinct**.

Write the letter that comes before each letter to decode the names of some endangered animals.

| A | B | C | D | E | F | G | H | I | J | K | L | M |
|---|---|---|---|---|---|---|---|---|---|---|---|---|
| N | O | P | Q | R | S | T | U | V | W | X | Y | Z |

T–F–B    M–J–P–O

_____

H–S–B–Z    X–P–M–G

_____

D–I–F–F–U–B–I

_____

C–M–B–D–L    S–I–J–O–P

_____

D–B–M–J–G–P–S–O–J–B    D–P–O–E–P–S

_____

C–B–M–E    F–B–H–M–F

_____

H–J–B–O–U    Q–B–O–E–B

_____

N–P–V–O–U–B–J–O    H–P–S–J–M–M–B

_____

B–G–S–J–D–B–O    F–M–F–Q–I–B–O–U

_____

Q–Z–H–N–Z    I–J–Q–Q–P

_____

**Be Curious**

Put some worms in a jar and carefully add some soil on top of them. Slowly pour in a little water and watch the worms. What did they do? Why?

# Science

Name _____

Write each animal name in the correct category.

| crocodile | canary | dog | sparrow | lizard |
| trout | toad | robin | tiger | shark |
| python | bear | guppy | salamander | newt |

**Mammals**          **Amphibians**          **Fish**

_____          _____          _____

_____          _____          _____

_____          _____          _____

**Reptiles**          **Birds**

_____          _____

_____          _____

_____          _____

Imagine that two animals combined to form a new species. Which two categories would each of the following represent?

ostricheetah          _____          _____

turtleopard          _____          _____

eelephant          _____          _____

frogorilla          _____          _____

pelicanteater          _____          _____

kangarooster          _____          _____

cardinalligator          _____          _____

cobratuna          _____          _____

**Be Curious**

Look for animal holes in a park or your yard. If you don't see any footprints, smooth some mud around the hole. Return the next day. What type of footprints do you see? If there are no footprints, could the hole belong to a snake?

# Science

Name _____

Insects have compound eyes, two antennae, zero to four wings, six legs, and three body parts. Draw an **X** on each insect.

Draw your own imaginary insect. Be sure to include all insect parts.

### Be Curious

Collect insects and other critters in a jar. Use a magnifying glass to closely examine their legs, wings, eyes, antennae, and body parts. Then set them free.

# Science

Name _____

Solve each rebus to write the names of the planets.

1. **P** + ![BLUE crayon] − **B** + ![shrimp] _____

2. ![mermaid] − **MAID** + **Q** + **R** + **E** _____

3. **S** + ![hat] + ![diamond] _____

4. **V** + ![peanuts] − **T** _____

5. **M** + **R** + **Z** _____

6. ![ear] + **TH** _____

7. **U** + ![rain cloud] + ![bus] − **B** _____

8. ![JUNE calendar] − **NE** + ![needle] − **N** + ![diamond] − **N** _____

9. ![net] − **T** + **P** + **2** + **N** _____

**Be Curious**

Read about the planets. Then use a large box to make a diorama of our solar system.

# Science

Name _____

Find the hidden matter in the spiral and write each one in the correct category. Start at the center.

**Solids**

_____  _____  _____

_____  _____  _____

_____  _____  _____

_____  _____  _____

_____  _____  _____

**Liquids**                                    **Gases**

_____  _____            _____

_____  _____            _____

_____  _____            _____

**Be Curious**

Watch as an adult boils water or makes coffee. See if you can name the solid, liquid, and gas.

# Science

Name _____

A meteorologist uses many weather words in a forecast. Underline the hidden word in each sentence. The first one is done for you.

| | | |
|---|---|---|
| thunder | humid | foggy |
| snow | downpour | rainy |
| chilly | sunshine | gusty |

1. Put a clo<u>th under</u> the can.

2. As the rain falls down, pour what's collected onto the plant.

3. I can see the sun shine brightly through the window.

4. Get the umbrellas now!

5. In the thick fog, gypsy moths are hard to find.

6. With all this rain, you feel like a fish.

7. Warm weather makes me hum idiotic, silly songs.

8. In August you often need to sit near a cool fan.

9. With this chill, you might catch a cold.

Unscramble other weather words.

1. itlghnngi _____

2. laih _____

3. ndaotor _____

4. ihrrcnaeu _____

5. lirzzdab _____

**Be Curious**
Use a can to collect rain or snow. See how long it takes to fill it to the top.

# Science

Name _____

Follow the directions to write the name of each dinosaur in the correct place on the grid.

Write . . .

| | | |
|---|---|---|
| **apatosaurus** in C2 | **trachodon** in A1 | **stegosaurus** in B3 |
| **triceratops** in A3 | **elasmosaurus** in C3 | **iguanodon** in A2 |
| **tyrannosaurus** in B1 | **pterosaur** in B2 | **brachiosaurus** in C1 |
| **allosaurus** in D3 | **protoceratops** in D1 | **ankylosaurus** in D2 |

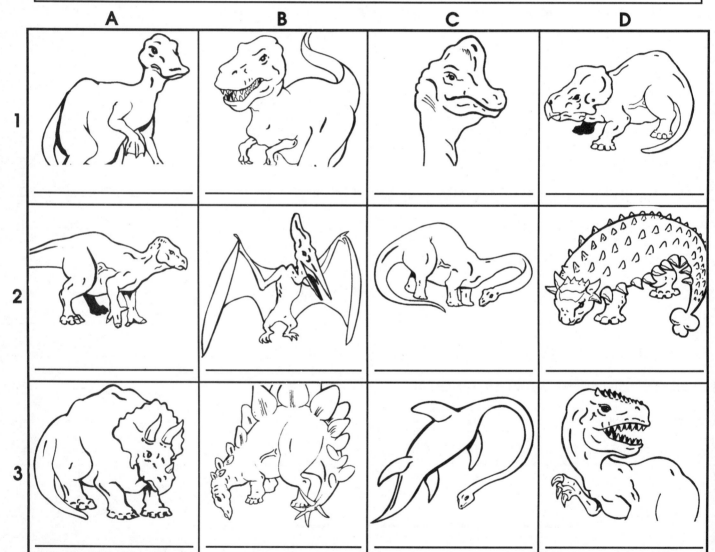

**Be Curious**

Cut out at least 20 teeth six inches long. Lay ten teeth in a row pointing down and ten pointing up beneath the first row. Use string to form a mouth around the teeth. Imagine a tyrannosaurus coming to eat you for dinner.

# Science

Name _____

Put an **X** on the word that does **not** make sense in the sentence. Write the word that should be in the sentence. **Hint:** It rhymes with the crossed-out word.

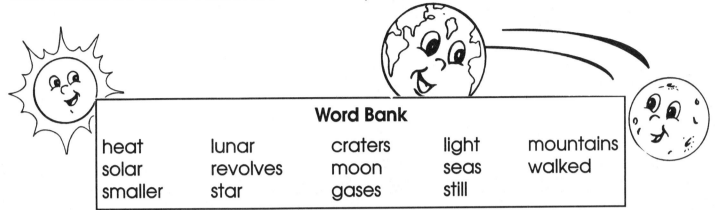

**Word Bank**

| | | | | |
|---|---|---|---|---|
| heat | lunar | craters | light | mountains |
| solar | revolves | moon | seas | walked |
| smaller | star | gases | still | |

1. The sun is Earth's brightest jar. _____

2. The moon has large freighters. _____

3. The Earth resolves around the sun. _____

4. The moon is taller than the Earth. _____

5. The sun is made up of hot glasses. _____

6. The word *pruner* refers to the moon. _____

7. The spoon travels around the Earth. _____

8. The moon reflects height from the sun. _____

9. The Earth gets meat and light from the sun. _____

10. Astronauts have squawked on the moon. _____

11. The sun stands chill. _____

12. The sun is the center of our polar system. _____

13. Fleas are flat areas on the moon. _____

14. The moon has large fountains. _____

**Be Curious**

Poke a sharp pencil through the middle of a paper plate. Push the pencil point into the ground. Use a crayon to mark the pencil's shadow on the paper plate. Check and mark the shadow every hour. What is happening?

# Science

Name _____

Draw the correct symbol for each habitat by each animal.

mountain   grassland   forest

desert   ocean   polar region

**Be Curious**
Go outside, sit down, and be very quiet. How many different animals can you see and hear?

# Science

Name _____

Be an energizer! Put the letters in correct numerical order to form words about energy. Then draw lines to match the words to their meanings.

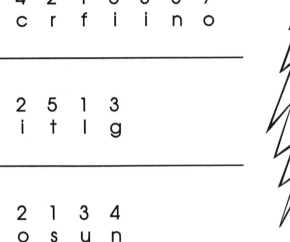

5 4 2 1 6 3 8 7
t c r f i i n o

_____

4 2 5 1 3
h i t l g

_____

5 2 1 3 4
d o s u n

_____

11 5 9 6 4 2 1 3 10 8 7
y t i r c l e e t c i

_____

2 3 5 1 4 6
h a o s d w

_____

4 2 1 3
l u f e

_____

a. form of energy used to run machines

b. object burned to give heat

c. a form of energy that you can see

d. made when an object blocks light

e. a form of energy that you can hear

f. rubbing two objects together

## Be Curious

In a quiet room, hold a paper cup to one ear and plug the other ear with a finger. What do you hear? Repeat using a glass. What do you hear now? Are the sounds you hear through the paper cup the same as the sounds you hear through the glass?

# Health

Name _____

Draw how your face would look in each situation.

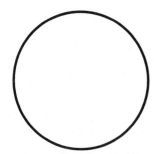

My team won a
baseball game.

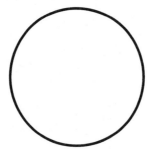

My puppy ran away.

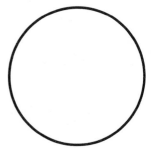

I can't find my
homework.

My favorite meal
is on the table.

I blew a 10-inch bubble
with my bubble gum.

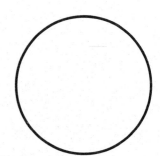

I don't know anyone
in the room.

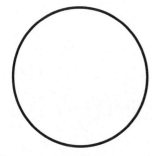

Someone tripped
me, and I fell.

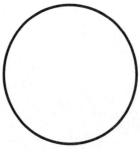

My family is proud
of my paper.

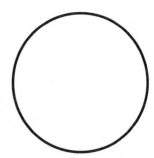

My goldfish died.

**Be Healthy**
Remember that it is healthy to feel different emotions, but a smile makes your
whole body feel good!

# Health

Name _____

Fill in the missing letter(s) in the foods in each group.

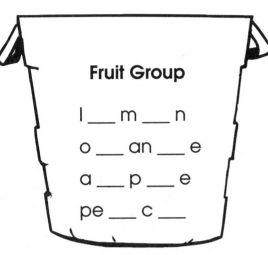

**Fruit Group**

l __ m __ n
o __ an __ e
a __ p __ e
pe __ c __

**Bread, Cereal, Rice, and Pasta Group**

r __ ll
cr __ ck __ r
m __ f __ __ n
m __ c __ r __ ni

**Milk, Yogurt, and Cheese Group**

b __ t __ e __
i __ e    cre __ m
m __ rga __ i __ e
sou __    __ rea __

**Poultry, Fish, Dry Beans, Eggs, Meat, and Nuts Group**

p __ r __          __ tea __
__ __ ick __ n      __ a __

**Vegetable Group**

c __ rr __ t      l __ tt __ ce
p __ t __ t __    br __ cc __ l __

My favorite foods are . . .

_____

_____

_____

**Be Healthy**

Remember that corn syrup is sweet, sugar may be sweeter, but a healthy body is sweetest of all.

# Health

Name _____

Exercise is important for a healthy body. Write the sport or activity on the line that matches each picture.

| Word Bank | | | |
|---|---|---|---|
| jogging | soccer | baseball | football |
| jumping | hockey | tennis | swimming |
| roller blading | | | |

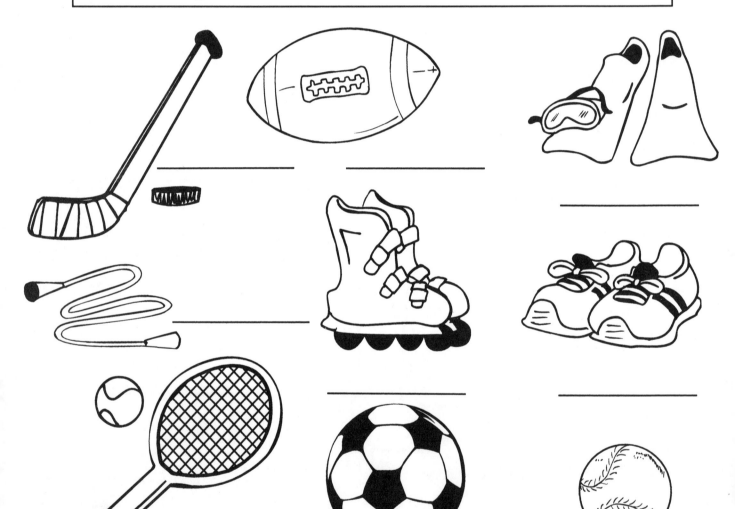

**Be Healthy**

For one month, keep track of when and how you exercised and the amount of time you spent doing this. Also write how long you watched TV each of those days. Which activity did you do the most—exercise or watch TV?

# Health

Name _____

Fill in the missing letters in each sentence to complete information about your body.

1. Your hea___t brings foo___ and oxyg___n to your cells.

2. Sto___ach juices br___ak dow___ fo___d.

3. B___nes help give your bod___ sh___pe.

4. L___ngs help you brea___he.

5. Ski___ prot___cts your insid___ org___ns.

6. Your bra___n contr___ls almost ever___thi___g your body doe___.

7. Most of your hai___ is not l___vi___g.

8. Bone___ are made up of liv___ng cell___.

9. Your skelet___n has 206 ___ones.

10. Saliv___ helps you swal___ow and diges___ food.

11. Muscl___s help your bod___ move.

12. The hea___t is your stron___est mus___le.

13. Kee___ clea___, ex___rcise, ea___ good ___ood, and get pl___nty
of res___ to sta___ heal___hy.

## Be Healthy
Make a list of your good health habits. Then make a list of your bad health habits. Which list is longer? How can you improve?

# Health

Name _____

Play "Teeth Trivia." Uncover facts about teeth by reading the scrambled words in a mirror. Then write the words correctly on the lines.

| | | |
|---|---|---|
| **enamel** covers the outside of each tooth. _____ | Enamel is the **hardest** tissue in your body. _____ | **plaque** can ruin a tooth's enamel. _____ |
| Under the enamel is dentin which is harder than **bone** _____ | Pulp contains the **nerves** _____ | The tooth's root holds it to the **gum** _____ |
| A child has 20 **primary** teeth. _____ | An adult has 32 **permanent** teeth. _____ | Too much sugar may cause **cavities** _____ |
| A cavity shows tooth **decay** _____ | Try to **floss** once each day. _____ | Brush your **teeth** after each meal. _____ |

## Be Healthy

Floss and brush your teeth daily. Visit your dentist twice a year. Once you have your **permanent** teeth they are friends meant to last a lifetime!

# Health

Name _____

Pretend that you are in a movie theater. List objects that your senses might notice.

**Seeing**

_____
_____
_____
_____
_____

**Smelling**

_____
_____
_____
_____
_____

**Hearing**

_____
_____
_____
_____
_____

**Tasting**

_____
_____
_____
_____
_____

**Touching**

_____
_____
_____
_____
_____

**Be Healthy**

With a partner, take turns putting different foods in a bag, one at a time, and guessing what each one is. When it is your turn to guess, cover your eyes and use the rest of your senses to identify the food.

# Health

Name _____

Make a mini-poster for each substance described below. Write the name of the substance below its matching poster.

**Word Bank**

medicine          alcohol
caffeine          nicotine
illegal drugs     aerosols/
                  pollutants

| Smoke is no joke!<br><br><br>Cigarettes stink! | Coffee, cola, and tea . . .<br><br><br>moderation is best, you see! | A mind's not clear if one drinks beer!<br><br><br>Think about it! |
| --- | --- | --- |
| _____ | _____ | _____ |
| Say "no" to drugs!<br><br><br>Say "yes" to clear thinking! | Take your medicine . . .<br><br><br>just as the doctor ordered! | Sniff only fresh air.<br><br><br>Keep your lungs and brain happy! |
| _____ | _____ | _____ |

**Be Healthy**
Teach others about good and bad substances by sharing your posters.

# Health

Name _____

Safety is very important for good health. Use the Word Bank to write the missing word in each sentence.

| Word Bank | | |
| --- | --- | --- |
| bathtub | poisonous | bicycle |
| buddy | helmet | kneepads |

1. Whenever you go swimming, always take a ☐☐☐☐☐ .

2. When riding a bike, you should wear a ☐☐☐☐☐☐ for protection.

3. ☐☐☐☐☐☐☐☐ protect your legs from injury when roller blading.

4. Never play with ☐☐☐☐☐☐☐☐☐ cleansers.

5. Never leave a baby brother or sister alone in the ☐☐☐☐☐☐☐ .

6. A ☐☐☐☐☐☐☐ is built for only one rider.

**Be Healthy**
Read all directions and safety messages on sports equipment and games before using them.

# Health

Name _____

Use the clue to solve each related health/safety situation. Write the answers on the lines.

1.     what a figure skater does during warm-ups

_____

2.     what good lighting makes reading

_____

3.     what lack of sleep may cause

_____

4.     an easy form of exercise

_____

5.     what healthy eating habits should eliminate

_____

6.     what you will say if you know the rules of a certain sport

_____

7.     what boxers need to avoid

_____

8.    a football player's dream

_____

9.    where a bicyclist must make a quick decision

_____

# Answer Key
## Second Grade
## in Review

Page 1

Page 2

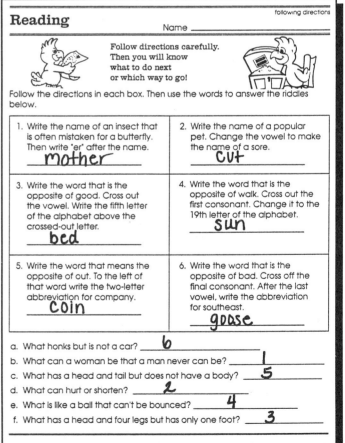

Page 3

## Page 4

 Hey, Mister,
What's the scoop?
Does it really
belong in that group?

Cross out the word in each group that does not belong. Then write the
headline that best describes the remaining words in that group.

### Headlines

| | | |
|---|---|---|
| Whole Holes | Flights in Space | Doggone It! |
| Going Around in Circles | Let's Run | Just Desserts! |
| Make Me Laugh! | Veggie Power | Legs Are Us |

**Legs Are Us**
giraffe
elephant
~~snake~~
ostrich

**Whole Holes**
doughnut
~~door~~
inner tube
Lifesaver

**Going Around in Circles**
~~box~~
wheel
Frisbee
hockey puck

**Doggone It!**
~~tabby~~
Poodle
Dalmatian
Irish setter

**Just Desserts!**
ice cream
pie
~~potatoes~~
cake

**Let's Run**
tag
races
jog
~~chess~~

**Make Me Laugh!**
clown
joke
~~house~~
cartoon

**Veggie Power**
~~watermelon~~
peas
spinach
carrots

**Flights in Space**
rocket ship
~~cloud~~
jet
Superman

---

## Page 5

 People can be funny!
In what little way?
Have you carefully listened
to what they may say?

**Idioms** are funny expressions that people say to "make a point."

Read each idiom and draw a funny picture about it. Then write a sentence
that tells what the idiom is supposed to mean.

| Example: | He has a green thumb. |
|---|---|
| It's raining cats and dogs! | **He grows plants well.** |
| Time flies! | Did you catch the train? |
| **Time goes by quickly.** | **Did you get to the** train on time? |
| Button your lip! | She has a frog in her throat. |
| **Be quiet!** | **She is hoarse.** |
| You really put your foot in your mouth! | Stop pulling my leg! |
| **You really said something** stupid! | **Stop teasing me!** |

---

## Page 6

Kay G. Detective needed to choose
all of the important clues.
When she went on an ocean cruise,
she discovered exciting news!

Kay found this letter taped to her cabin door. Read it and answer the questions.

Dear Miss Detective,

When I awoke at sunrise, I found a very special guest
hiding in my room. At first, I thought I might dye, but now
I no better. I promised to take him to the Emerald Island when
our ship passes it in mid-afternoon.

Please don't get soar, but I need your help! If you
follow my directions carefully, we can help my new friend.

1. Lift up your bed.
2. Crawl through the special tunnel underneath.
3. Walk down a dozen steps. We will be waiting for
you at the bottom with a raft.

sincerely,
Bea Friend

P.S. I misspelled three words to give you a clue about my guest.

1. About what time did Bea discover
her uninvited guest?
   (a) 6:00 A.M.
   b. 10:00 A.M.
   c. 5:00 P.M.

2. Where were Kay G. and Bea?
   a. on an airplane
   (b) on a cruise ship
   c. on an island

3. What three words were spelled
incorrectly in the letter?
   dye
   no
   soar

4. What had Bea found in her
cabin? **dinosaur**

---

## Page 7

 Ivan Openmind will often pause
to think what really was the cause,
while Seymour Clearly's thoughts must collect
to see what became the effect.

Choose from the **causes** or the **effects** to complete each sentence.

**Ivan Openmind's Causes**

Because Otto McCanic made a slight mistake, . . .

When Miss B.U. Tifful forgot to wear makeup, . . .

Because Lotta Suds put too much soap in the washing machine, . . .

**Seymour Clearly's Effects**

she handed in her dad's blueprints as homework.

the robot could do her chores and homework while she relaxed.

his cats barked and his dogs meowed.

the director of the play had a fit.

1. **Because Lotta Suds put too much soap in the washing machine,**
the laundry room was filled with bubbles.

2. When Ken L. Keeper mixed up the dog and cat food, **his cats barked and his dogs meowed.**

3. **Because Otto McCanic made a slight mistake,**
the car could only go backwards.

4. Because Ima Genius invented a robot, **the robot did her chores and homework while she relaxed.**

5. Because Flora Getfull grabbed the wrong papers off the desk, **she handed in her dad's blueprints as homework.**

6. When Otto B. Estar forgot his lines again, **the director of the play had a fit.**

7. **When Miss B.U. Tifful forgot to wear make-up,**
her fans didn't recognize her.

---

104                    IF8784 Second Grade in Review

A fact is real,
while fiction is not.
Place each phrase below
in the right spot.

Write the number of each phrase on a windowsill in the proper building. Then draw its picture in the window.

1. giant with three eyes
2. round basketball
3. spotted dog
4. chocolate sundae
5. purple monkey
6. wide-screen television
7. frog prince
8. flying cat
9. magic lamp
10. mother and father
11. shiny bicycle
12. fire-breathing dragon

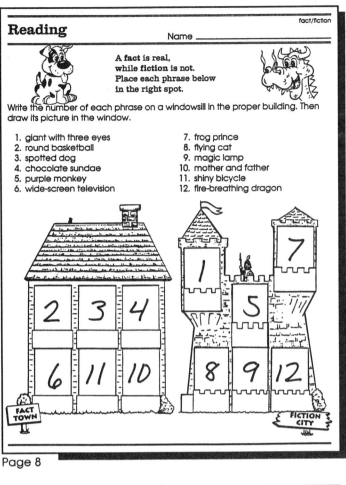

FACT TOWN

FICTION CITY

---

How does dragon relate to cave,
or queen relate to king?
How does knight relate to night?
Let's do some careful thinking.

**Analogies** show how words are related.

Example: **Dragon** is to **cave** as **bear** is to **den**.

Put on your thinking cap and write the missing word to each analogy.

1. Fingers are to **hands** as toes are to ___feet___.
2. Box is to **square** as globe is to ___round___.
3. Milk is to **drink** as bread is to ___eat___.
4. Laugh is to **happy** as cry is to ___sad___.
5. Run is to **ran** as draw is to ___drew___.
6. Lion is to **jungle** as fish is to ___sea___.
7. Mother is to **father** as sister is to ___brother___.
8. Crayon is to **draw** as pencil is to ___write___.
9. Run is to **walk** as play is to ___work___.
10. Day is to **week** as month is to ___year___.
11. Scale is to **weigh** as ruler is to ___measure___.
12. Teacher is to **school** as nurse is to ___hospital___.
13. Dog is to **puppy** as cat is to ___kitten___.
14. Apple is to **red** as banana is to ___yellow___.
15. Car is to **garage** as jet is to ___hangar___.

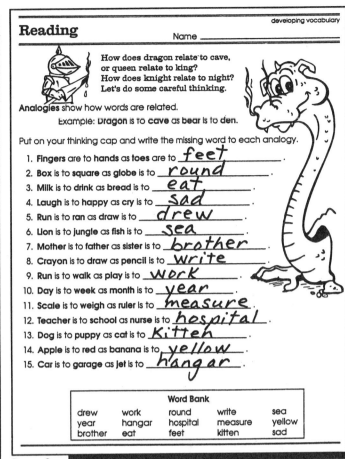

| Word Bank | | | | |
|---|---|---|---|---|
| drew | work | round | write | sea |
| year | hangar | hospital | measure | yellow |
| brother | eat | feet | kitten | sad |

---

Elongated words
make one shiver and shake,
but if you read everything else
they're a piece of cake!

Carefully read the story on this and the next page. Fill in the missing words in the story by picking the words in the box that mean the same as the words beneath the lines. **Hint:** It helps to read past the missing word to understand the meaning.

(1) near, far away
(2) thought, known
(3) small, horrible
(4) lived in, hated
(5) huge, tiny
(6) ran, yelled
(7) eaten, met
(8) story, bells
(9) pile, group
(10) met, hopped
(11) little, green
(12) tongue, bite
(13) good, sour
(14) giggle, cry
(15) alone, happy
(16) worry, laugh
(17) buy, eat
(18) nearing, leaving
(19) hit, covered
(20) brave, tired
(21) exactly, double
(22) enemy, friend
(23) strong, nice
(24) friendly, nasty
(25) wisely, easily
(26) frowned, smiled
(27) spread, stopped
(28) bothered, liked

Long ago in a (1) ___faraway___ (remote) kingdom on the other side of the world, it was (2) ___thought___ (rumored) that a mean and (3) ___horrible___ (horrendous) giant and his large family (4) ___lived in___ (inhabited) a (5) ___huge___ (mammoth) castle. Whenever thundering footsteps shook the ground, people quickly (6) ___ran___ (scampered) in the opposite direction. No one had actually (7) ___met___ (encountered) the giant, but everyone seemed to have heard the (8) ___story___ (narrative).

One day a (9) ___group___ (cluster) of children (10) ___met___ (assembled) near the giant's castle. They all began teasing a (11) ___little___ (diminutive) boy named PeeWee.

---

(Continued)

"You're so tiny that you'd hardly make an itty-bitty (12) ___bite___ (morsel) in the giant's mouth!" yelled Sluggo. "I bet you wouldn't even taste (13) ___good___ (palatable).

Poor little PeeWee began to quietly (14) ___cry___ (blubber). Then the other children ran away, leaving the sad, little boy (15) ___alone___ (solitary).

PeeWee began to (16) ___worry___ (fret) about the giant.

"What if he wants to (17) ___eat___ (devour) me?" he thought.

Suddenly, PeeWee heard footsteps (18) ___nearing___ (approaching). He (19) ___covered___ (enveloped) his eyes with his hands.

After a minute he became (20) ___brave___ (dauntless) enough to open his eyes. Standing before him was a boy (21) ___exactly___ (precisely) his size.

"My name is Herbie," said the boy. "I live in that castle. Please be my (22) ___friend___ (confidant). You seem so (23) ___nice___ (amiable), unlike the others. My father is a giant, but he is (24) ___friendly___ (congenial) and kind. He told me to choose my friends (25) ___wisely___ (sensibly)."

PeeWee (26) ___smiled___ (beamed) and became the boy's friend.

News of PeeWee's friendship with the giant's son soon (27) ___spread___ (diffused) throughout the kingdom . . . and from that day on, no one ever (28) ___bothered___ (perturbed) PeeWee again.

---

Name _____

If you spread the peanut butter
before you get the bread,
your fingers will stick together,
and there'll be trouble ahead!

Number each set of sentences 1, 2, and 3 in the correct order.

**3** Go home to get clean clothes.
**2** Fall in a muddy puddle.
**1** Try to be cool and jump over a big, muddy puddle.

**1** Start to clean a very messy bedroom at 9:00 a.m.
**3** Go back to the bedroom to finish cleaning at 1:00 p.m.
**2** Eat a big lunch at noon.

**1** Learn a silly joke.
**2** Tell the joke to your friends.
**3** Watch your audience laugh loudly.

**3** Place the roller blades in the closet.
**1** Put on brand-new roller blades.
**2** Skate until your feet hurt.

**3** Carefully rub your sore tummy.
**2** Eat the candy very quickly.
**1** Buy lots of yummy candy at the store.

**2** Swing the bat carefully.
**1** Walk to home plate with a bat.
**3** Hit the ball hard and run.

Page 12

---

Name _____

 A weatherman prepares ahead,
and you can do this, too.
Just study very carefully
each and every clue.

Decide what will happen next by underlining the sentence that would best complete each cartoon strip. Then draw a picture to show that sentence.

a. Magician pulls a rabbit from his hat.
b. Magician puts the hat on his head.

a. The children go ice skating at the park.
b. The children put a hat on the snowman's head.

a. The organ grinder slips on a banana peel.
b. The organ grinder begins to sing.

Page 13

---

Name _____

 Can you always
believe what you read,
or does information
sometimes mislead?

Read each newspaper article. Then circle the answer to each question.

**Inventor Takes Flight**

"You'll feel lighter than air!" exclaimed Dr. I.M. Uphigh.

The well-known inventor recently created a special shoe. Its secret lies in the soles. Hundreds of little rubber balls are placed tightly inside the rubber soles. Whenever a person feels like flying, he just bounces on his feet and up he goes! "You'll have a ball!" Uphigh told the surprised reporters.

1. What is Dr. Uphigh's occupation?
   a. dentist   b. pilot   (c. inventor)

2. What makes his shoes special?
   a. rubber soles   (b. rubber balls)
   c. bright lights

3. Where would his invention work best?
   (a. on cement)   b. in mud
   c. in a lake

1. What was special about Mr. Shore?
   a. He was king of a sand castle.
   b. He was mayor.
   (c. He built sand castles.)

2. How long did he live in his castle?
   a. 8 days   b. 38 days   (c. 83 days)

3. What happened to the castle?
   (a. Rain destroyed it.)
   b. The mayor bought it.
   c. Mr. Shore moved it to a new place.

**Our City's Own Sandman**

Mr. C. Shore has won a bet with our mayor. He proved that a man's castle is his home. For 83 days he lived on the beach in his own castle made from wet sand. During his stay, Mr. Shore said, "I feel like a king."

Mr. Shore's reign finally ended when a huge rainstorm invaded his kingdom, and his castle by the sea quickly disappeared.

Page 14

---

Name _____

Old Farmer McFarkle
had a farm
where inventions he made
which worked like a charm.

Read about Farmer McFarkle's farm. Circle the letter that states the main idea of each paragraph.

1. Farmer McFarkle built a very modern barn. Inside the barn he put a food machine for the animals. When they were hungry, the animals pushed a button and out popped fruit, vegetables, or hay. The clever farmer even installed speakers so that the animals could listen to "Old McFarkle Had a Farm" or "The Sound of Moosic."
   a. Speakers play music in a barn.
   (b) McFarkle built a modern barn.
   c. The animals ate healthy farm food.

2. Cowabunga Cow gave the McFarkle family lots of milk every day. Her milk was wonderful because it came in different flavors—vanilla, chocolate, and strawberry. On cold days she even gave Neapolitan ice cream!
   a. Cowabunga was a cow that loved milk.
   b. Cowabunga was a white, brown, and pink cow.
   (c) Cowabunga was a cow that made special milk.

3. Farmer McFarkle, tired of the eggs falling from the nests and cracking on the floor, had his hens sit on boxes instead of nests. After awhile, the hens began to lay square eggs that didn't roll.
   (a) McFarkle solved a problem.
   b. McFarkle had square hens.
   c. McFarkle ate eggs for breakfast.

4. The pigs on the McFarkle farm loved to roll in the mud. Farmer McFarkle didn't want to spoil their fun, but he did want his farm to be clean and tidy. So he built a pig shower. When pigs stepped onto a rolling belt, it moved them toward the shower where they were sprayed clean.
   a. The pigs enjoyed rolling in the mud.
   b. The pigs ate too much.
   (c) McFarkle discovered a way to clean dirty pigs.

Page 15

---

# English

Name _____

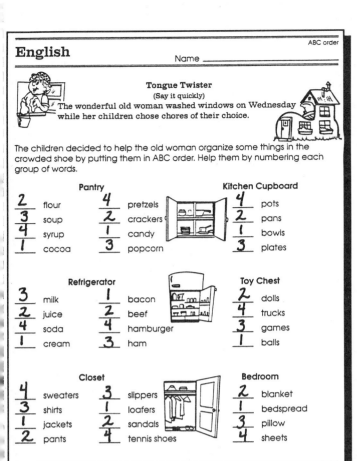

**Tongue Twister**
(Say it quickly)
The wonderful old woman washed windows on Wednesday while her children chose chores of their choice.

The children decided to help the old woman organize some things in the crowded shoe by putting them in ABC order. Help them by numbering each group of words.

**Pantry**
2 flour
3 soup
4 syrup
1 cocoa

4 pretzels
2 crackers
1 candy
3 popcorn

**Kitchen Cupboard**
4 pots
2 pans
1 bowls
3 plates

**Refrigerator**
3 milk
2 juice
4 soda
1 cream

1 bacon
2 beef
4 hamburger
3 ham

**Toy Chest**
2 dolls
4 trucks
3 games
1 balls

**Closet**
4 sweaters
3 shirts
1 jackets
2 pants

3 slippers
1 loafers
2 sandals
4 tennis shoes

**Bedroom**
2 blanket
1 bedspread
3 pillow
4 sheets

---

# English

Name _____

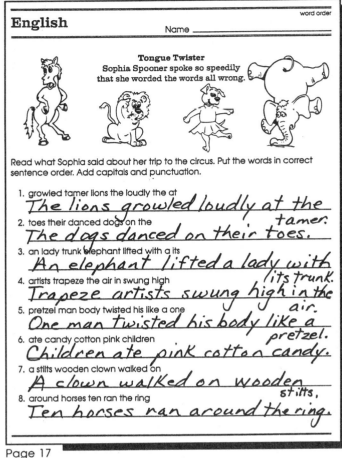

**Tongue Twister**
Sophia Spooner spoke so speedily
that she worded the words all wrong.

Read what Sophia said about her trip to the circus. Put the words in correct sentence order. Add capitals and punctuation.

1. growled tamer lions the loudly the at
   *The lions growled loudly at the tamer.*

2. toes their danced dogs on the
   *The dogs danced on their toes.*

3. an lady trunk elephant lifted with a its
   *An elephant lifted a lady with its trunk.*

4. artists trapeze the air in swung high
   *Trapeze artists swung high in the air.*

5. pretzel man body twisted his like a one
   *One man twisted his body like a pretzel.*

6. ate candy cotton pink children
   *Children ate pink cotton candy.*

7. a stilts wooden clown walked on
   *A clown walked on wooden stilts.*

8. around horses ten ran the ring
   *Ten horses ran around the ring.*

---

# English

Name _____

**Tongue Twister**
Cindy Sue selected cereal that provided
proper prizes with proper proof of purchase.

Discover what toy prizes Cindy chose by writing the letter that comes **before** each letter below. The prizes are all nouns which name people, places, or things.

puppet (qvqqfu)

kite (ljuf)

boat (cpbu)

truck (usvdl)

plane (qmbof)

ring (sjoh)

clay (dmbz)

marble (nbscmf)

watch (xbudi)

kitten (ljuufo)

hoop (ippq)

ball (cbmm)

---

# English

Name _____

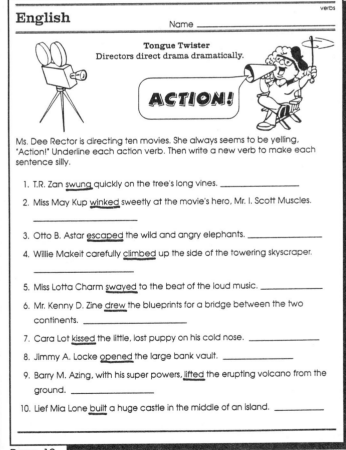

**Tongue Twister**
Directors direct drama dramatically.

ACTION!

Ms. Dee Rector is directing ten movies. She always seems to be yelling, "Action!" Underline each action verb. Then write a new verb to make each sentence silly.

1. T.R. Zan swung quickly on the tree's long vines. _____

2. Miss May Kup winked sweetly at the movie's hero, Mr. I. Scott Muscles.
   _____

3. Otto B. Astar escaped the wild and angry elephants. _____

4. Willie Makeit carefully climbed up the side of the towering skyscraper.
   _____

5. Miss Lotta Charm swayed to the beat of the loud music. _____

6. Mr. Kenny D. Zine drew the blueprints for a bridge between the two
   continents. _____

7. Cara Lot kissed the little, lost puppy on his cold nose. _____

8. Jimmy A. Locke opened the large bank vault. _____

9. Barry M. Azing, with his super powers, lifted the erupting volcano from the
   ground. _____

10. Lief Mia Lone built a huge castle in the middle of an island. _____

---

**Tongue Twister**
Reflections reveal realistic reproductions.

Mirrors are like copy machines. Write the plural for each noun. Then draw each reflection in the mirror.

elf _elves_   fox _foxes_   cherry _cherries_

mouse _mice_   watch _watches_   leaf _leaves_

lady _ladies_   child _children_   ball _balls_

bunny _bunnies_   tooth _teeth_   box _boxes_

---

**Tongue Twister**
Quiz your acquaintances with quick, inquiring questions.

Someone's been asking Mother Goose some questions, and she's been telling some secrets. Add a period to each statement and a question mark to each question. Then, write the letter of each statement or question next to its matching sentence.

_g_ He spilled ink all over himself .

_b_ Why did Humpty Dumpty fall ?

_a_ A fly had flown into her bowl .

_c_ Why was Mary quite contrary ?

_f_ Where were Little Bo Peep's sheep ?

_h_ The clock struck one .

_e_ Why did London Bridge fall down ?

_d_ Why did Little Jack Horner sit in the corner ?

a. Why did the spider sit by Little Miss Muffet ?

b. Someone greased the wall .

c. The bunnies had eaten her flowers .

d. He ate too many of his mother's pies .

e. Its braces needed tightening .

f. They were selling their wool at the market .

g. Why was Little Boy blue ?

h. Why did the mouse run down the clock ?

---

**Tongue Twister**
Sherlock shadowed the shadow of the shifty, shameless, short, sharp-nosed shoplifter.

Sherlock always looked for the true meaning of each clue so he would not make a mistake. Find the incorrect meaning of each word and underline it.

1. hard
   a. not soft
   b. shiny
   c. difficult

2. pet
   a. tame animal
   b. pat gently
   c. a deep hole

3. seal
   a. a type of boat
   b. a sea mammal
   c. to close completely

4. file
   a. tool used for grinding
   b. to arrange papers in order
   c. to take up a whole space

5. star
   a. a distant sun
   b. to look at steadily
   c. actor in leading role

6. fly
   a. an insect
   b. move through the air
   c. an instrument

7. dough
   a. to dig a hole
   b. slang for money
   c. mixture of flour and water

8. right
   a. opposite of left
   b. to use a pencil
   c. correct

9. basket
   a. score made by tossing a ball through a net
   b. a container
   c. part of a wall

10. down
    a. opposite of up
    b. soft feathers
    c. pile of sand

11. ball
    a. metal object that rings
    b. a round object
    c. a formal dance

12. cool
    a. a little cold
    b. a fuel
    c. calm

---

**Tongue Twister**
The shoes on the shelves have similar shapes, but the shoes on the dock are different.

**Synonyms** have similar meanings. **Antonyms** are opposites. Write a synonym for each word in a shoe on a shelf. Write an antonym for each word in a shoe on a dock. Use the Word Bank.

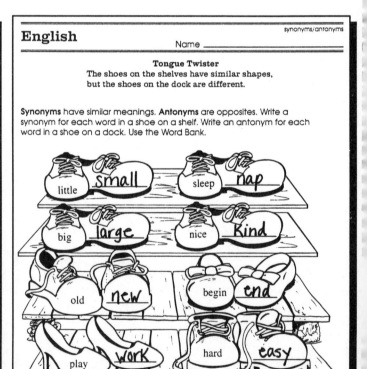

little _small_   sleep _nap_

big _large_   nice _kind_

old _new_   begin _end_

play _work_   hard _easy_

| Word Bank | | | |
|---|---|---|---|
| end | skinny | easy | nap |
| silly | pretty | work | kind |
| new | small | down | large |

---

# English

Name _____

**Tongue Twister**
Tennessee tightly tensed up the
tension on his tennis racket.

Verb tense tells when an action occurs: in the past, at the present time, or in the future. Write the correct verb for each sentence.

1. At yesterday's match the boxer ___**proved**___ himself to be a real dog.
   (prove, proved, proving)

2. The baseball player ___**went**___ to jail because he stole a base.
   (go, went, going)

3. The golfer is ___**changing**___ his pants because he got a hole in one.
   (change, changed, changing)

4. The football players ___**stay**___ cool because they have many fans.
   (stay, stayed, staying)

5. The only thing the fisherman ___**caught**___ was a cold.
   (catches, caught, catching)

6. The waitress is ___**thinking**___ about becoming a tennis player because she serves so well.
   (think, thought, thinking)

7. The deep sea diver ___**brings**___ peanut butter in case he catches a jellyfish.
   (brings, brought, bringing)

8. The fisherman ___**decided**___ not to clean the fish because it had been in water all day.
   (decide, decided, deciding)

9. The runner is fast because he ___**has**___ athlete's foot.
   (has, had, having)

10. The basketball player ___**promised**___ to help the Easter Bunny because he stuffs baskets so well.
    (promise, promised, promising)

Page 24

---

# English

Name _____

**Tongue Twister**
Owen owned the only oboe in Ohio.

A noun can show ownership by adding **'s** or **s'**. If the noun is singular, add **'s**. If the noun is plural, add **s'**. Add apostrophes in the sentences where needed.

1. Can a piano's key open anything?

2. Tim's tuba would be lighter if it were a *one-ba*.

3. Does a fish's scale sound better than a singer's scale?

4. The conductor's watch keeps time to the music.

5. The orchestra's favorite dessert is *cello*.

6. Some musicians' teeth sparkle because they use a *tuba* toothpaste.

7. The violin's bow makes it more present-able.

8. A rubber band's music has lots of snap!

9. Does a baseball player's pitch help him sing better?

10. That musician's favorite Christmas treat is *flute-cake*.

Page 25

---

# Spelling

Name _____

Clementine Clown loves to dress in very silly clothing. Fill in the blanks with the missing short vowels to spell what she is wearing.

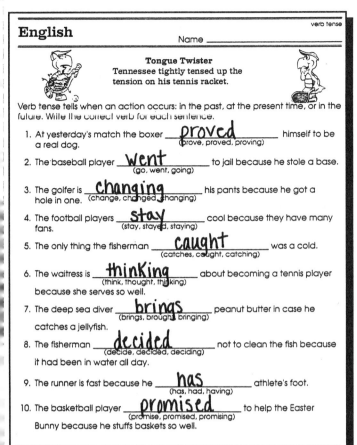

b**i**g s**u**ngl**a**ss**e**s

s**i**lly n**e**cklace

y**e**llow r**i**bb**o**n

dr**e**ss w**i**th f**a**t c**a**ts

ch**e**ckered s**o**cks

pl**a**st**i**c s**a**nd**a**l

**Just for Laughs**
Why d**i**d Cl**a**ncy y**e**ll wh**e**n Cl**e**m**e**ntine pr**e**ssed h**i**s p**a**nts?
*Because he was st**i**ll **i**n th**e**m!*

Page 26

---

# Spelling

Name _____

See what Sadie ate by unscrambling the letters to write words with long vowel sounds.

sk**ā**te
p**ō**ny
pl**ā**ne
g**ō**at
p**ē**ach
st**ō**ve
l**ī**ght
ph**ō**ne
gl**ō**be
t**ī**ger
t**ī**re
pr**ū**ne
tr**ā**y
c**ū**be
g**ā**te

**Just for Laughs**
How did S**a**die f**ee**l after sh**e** swallowed her **o**wn t**a**il?
*L**ī**ke sh**e** was g**o**ing around in circles.*

Page 27

---

# Spelling

Name _____

Write the missing consonant blends and you will see what the Trash Monster gave each of his friends.

| br | cl | dr | fr | gr | pr | sn | spr | str |
|----|----|----|----|----|----|----|-----|-----|
| bl | cr | fl | gl | pl | scr | sp | st | tr |

**Humpty Dumpty**
g**l**ue
p**l**aster
first-aid **cr**eam
safety **str**ap

**Little Miss Muffet**
**st**ool
**sp**oon
**cl**eam
**sp**ider **spr**ay

**Cinderella**
**br**oom
**sl**ippers
**cl**ock
**cr**own
**pr**ince

**Old Mother Hubbard**
**br**ead
**cr**ackers
**fr**uitcake
**fr**ankfurters
**st**ew

**Mary, Mary Quite Contrary**
**fl**owers
**pl**ants
**bl**ossoms

**Frog Prince**
**cr**icket
**dr**agonflies
**fl**ies

**Three Little Pigs**
**str**aw
**st**icks
**br**icks
**st**eel
**gr**anite

**Just for Laughs**
Why did the **Tr**ash Monster **st**and outside the furniture p**l**ant?

*He was* **sn***ooping for table* **scr***aps!*

---

# Spelling

Name _____

Write the final consonant blend for each word. Color each toe by blending the colors shown on Ernest's Color Chart.

| Ernest's Color Chart | | |
|---|---|---|
| **ft** = blue/red | **nd** = yellow/brown | **nt** = yellow/red |
| **lt** = purple/red | **nk** = yellow/green | **pt** = orange/red |
| **mp** = pink/orange | **ld** = purple/brown | **st** = black/red |

CHE**ST**  QUI**LT**  HAN**LT**(D)  SPLI**NT**  TRA**MP**  SHI**FT**

BLO**ND**  SLE**PT**  YA**NK**  PAI**NT**  HAU**NT**  THE**FT**

TWI**ST**  BRA**ND**  SLA**NT**

FAI**NT**  CHI**LD**(MP)  FA**ST**

**Just for Laughs**
Where did Erne**st** ho**ld** his gra**nd** opening?
*In a toe truck*

---

# Spelling

Name _____

Use the clues to write the correct double consonant (**ff**, **ss**, **ll**, or **zz**) at the end of each word.

1. che**ss** = a game
2. hi**ll** = a small mountain
3. le**ss** = not more
4. pu**ff** = small cloud of smoke
5. hi**ss** = snake noise
6. cu**ff** = bottom of sleeve
7. fi**zz** = bubbles in a drink
8. se**ll** = opposite of buy
9. fu**zz** = lint on sweater
10. gu**ll** = a sea bird
11. ra**zz** = to tease
12. me**ss** = clutter
13. ye**ll** = to scream
14. gla**ss** = holds a drink
15. du**ll** = not sharp
16. sni**ff** = to smell
17. we**ll** = not sick
18. bu**zz** = bee's sound
19. pi**ll** = tablet
20. dre**ss** = gown

**Just for Laughs**
What do you ca**ll** twins who walk acro**ss** the baseba**ll** diamond stu**ff**ed inside the same shirt? *A double-header*

---

# Spelling

Name _____

Add a word to make a **compound word** with both the word on the left and the word on the right. Then complete the riddle by writing the boxed letters in the correct blanks.

| Word Bank | | | |
|---|---|---|---|
| ground | room | watch | cup |
| wheel | ball | drop | fire |
| suit | moon | sand | fly |
| yard | neck | paper | book |

wrist **Watch** dog
camp **fire** wood
foot **ball** room
pin **wheel** chair
rain **drop** out
fire **fly** paper
honey **moon** light
mush **room** mate

swim **suit** case
under **ground** hog
quick **sand** man
turtle **neck** lace
note **book** worm
sand **paper** boy
back **yard** stick
butter **cup** cake

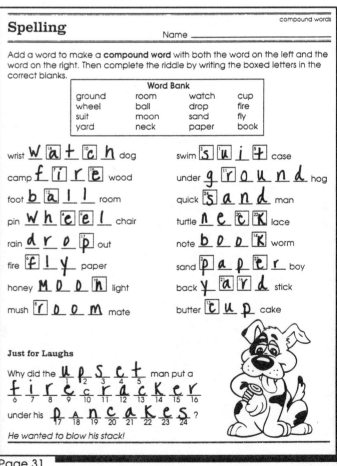

**Just for Laughs**
Why did the **upset** man put a **firecracker** under his **pancakes**?
*He wanted to blow his stack!*

---

IF8784 Second Grade in Review

## Page 32

### Spelling
contractions

Name _____

Write the contraction for each pair of cars.

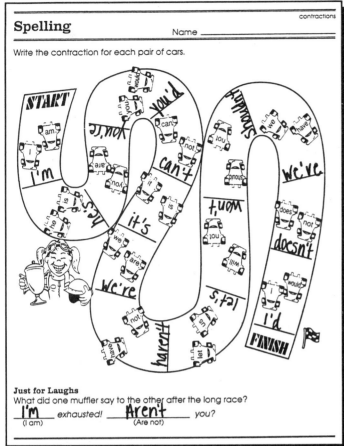

**Just for Laughs**

What did one muffler say to the other after the long race?

__I'm__ (I am) exhausted! __Aren't__ (Are not) you?

---

## Page 33

### Spelling
silent letters

Name _____

Shhhh! Write the silent letter (**b, g, k, t,** or **w**) missing from each word.

**W**rinkle

lam**b**     clim**b**

**K**nit

wa**t**ch     **W**rap

**W**rite

**K**nee     ca**t**ch

**g**nome

thum**b**     **K**now

**W**rong     com**b**     **W**rist

**Just for Laughs**

How did the reporter **K** now where the monkey clim **b** ed?

*He wa* **t** *ched the monkey and dictated his findings into an ape recorder.*

---

## Page 34

### Spelling
homophones

Name _____

Listen carefully! Unscramble the scrambled homophone and write it on the line.

hare – rhai → **hair**

wood – wlduo → **would**

wear – eerhw → **where**

write – trhgi → **right**

ant – utna → **aunt**

male – lmai → **mail**

cent – nsect → **scent**

sum – seom → **some**

ate – htieg → **eight**

blue – lwbe → **blew**

rays – seair → **raise**

pear – iarp → **pair**

**Just for Laughs**

What may happen if you call a __bee__ (ebe) family on a telephone?

__There__ (htree) may __be__ (eb) a buzzy signal. __their__ (trehi)

---

## Page 35

### Spelling
suffixes

Name _____

Read each story ending. Use the Word Bank to add a suffix to the end of each base word and write the new word on the line.

**Word Bank**

| | | |
|---|---|---|
| ness | est | s |
| ed | er | ful |

1. . . . and the __poorest__ (poor) boy of all went to live in the castle.

2. . . . and the little elf __disappeared__ (disappear) into the thick forest.

3. . . . and the clever mouse __proved__ (prove) himself to be __smarter__ (smart) than the huge lion.

4. . . . and the baby elephant finally __returned__ (return) to his mother.

5. . . . and the __Kindness__ (kind) of the old woman __filled__ (fill) their hearts with joy.

6. . . . and the __surprised__ (surprise) frog __jumped__ (jump) __higher__ (high) than all of the __clouds__ (cloud) and was never seen again.

7. . . . and the lazy dragon became the __fattest__ (fat) creature in the kingdom.

8. . . . and the wise king __continued__ (continue) to share his gold with the poor people.

**Just for Laughs**

How can you tell that many clock __makers__ (maker) __invented__ (invent) fairy tales?

*Each story* __begins__ (begin) *with "Once upon a time . . ."*

---

## Page 36

# Spelling

Name _____

Complete each riddle by writing a day of the week in the blank.

**Word Bank**

| | | |
|---|---|---|
| Friday | Thursday | Saturday |
| Sunday | Wednesday | Tuesday |
| Monday | | |

1. I'm two days before the first day of the weekend.
   I am __Thursday__ .

2. I come in second on the calendar and in alphabetical order.
   I am __Monday__ .

3. Although I stand in the middle of the school week, I am last when placed in alphabetical order. I am __Wednesday__ .

4. Although calendars show me as the first day of the week, many consider me the last day of the weekend. I am __Sunday__ .

5. I may be the first day when arranged in alphabetical order, but I am the last day of school before the weekend. I am __Friday__ .

6. I am spaced exactly in the middle between Sunday and Thursday.
   I am __Tuesday__ .

7. Depending on how you looked at it, I am either the last day of the week or the first day of the weekend. I am __Saturday__ .

Now rewrite the days of the week in the order they are shown on a calendar.

1. __Sunday__        5. __Thursday__
2. __Monday__        6. __Friday__
3. __Tuesday__       7. __Saturday__
4. __Wednesday__

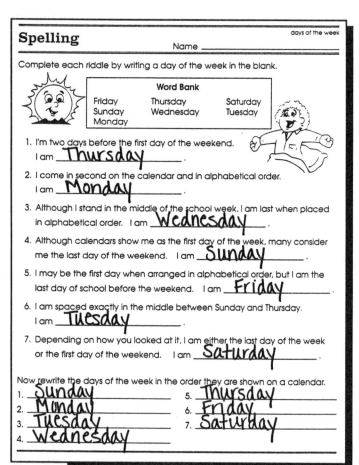

---

## Page 37

# Spelling

Name _____

Use the clues to write the name of each month.

1. __Ap__ ril
   (a monkey minus e)
2. Sept __ember__
   (burning coal)
3. __March__
   (to lift knees high while walking)
4. Aug __us__ t
   (not them)
5. Dec __ember__
   (member minus the first m)
6. __Jul__ y
   (short for Julie)
7. Oc __to__ ber
   (part of foot minus e)
8. __Jan__ uary
   (nickname for Janice)
9. __June__
   (rhymes with tune)
10. __Feb__ ruary
    (rhymes with web)
11. __Nove__ mber
    (rhymes with stove)
12. __May__ I?
    (asking permission)

Write the names of the months in order.

1. __January__        7. __July__
2. __February__       8. __August__
3. __March__          9. __September__
4. __April__         10. __October__
5. __May__           11. __November__
6. __June__          12. __December__

**Just for Laughs**
What does Tarzan sing in __December__ ?

"Jungle Bells"

---

## Page 38

# Spelling

Name _____

Color the letters that form each word's abbreviation. Then write the abbreviation on the line. Don't forget the period!

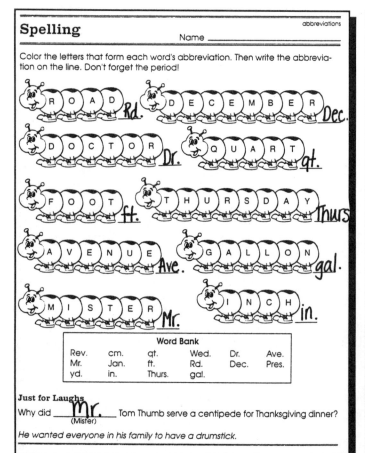

ROAD __Rd.__    DECEMBER __Dec.__

DOCTOR __Dr.__    QUART __qt.__

FOOT __ft.__    THURSDAY __Thurs__

AVENUE __Ave.__    GALLON __gal.__

MISTER __Mr.__    INCH __in.__

**Word Bank**

| | | | | |
|---|---|---|---|---|
| Rev. | cm. | qt. | Wed. | Dr. | Ave. |
| Mr. | Jan. | ft. | Rd. | Dec. | Pres. |
| yd. | in. | Thurs. | gal. | | |

**Just for Laughs**
Why did __Mr.__ Tom Thumb serve a centipede for Thanksgiving dinner?
(Mister)

He wanted everyone in his family to have a drumstick.

---

## Page 39

# Spelling

Name _____

These extraordinary spiders wear different colored socks on their unusual, long legs. Color those socks that contain a base word that can correctly join with the prefix in the spider's body to make a word.

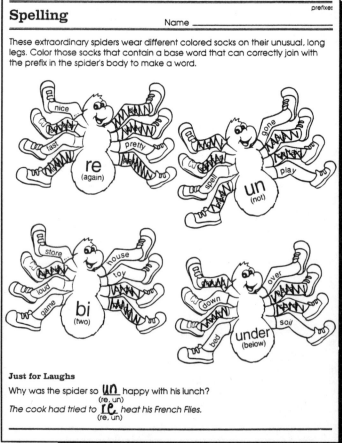

**Just for Laughs**
Why was the spider so __un__ happy with his lunch?
(re, un)
The cook had tried to __re__ heat his French Flies.
(re, un)

---

# Creative Writing

Name _____

You have been selected by Bowser Biscuits Dog Food to write a TV commercial advertising an exciting, new puppy food. After discussing the project with your puppy, Puddles, you know exactly what to write to convince the world that this product is best.

Write your commercial. Be sure to include the name of the product, the reason it is so special, its cost, and where it may be purchased.

*Answers will vary.*

**Make Someone Smile**
Write a question for the riddle.

Question: _____

_____

Answer:  *Pupperoni Pizza, Muttzarella Cheese, and Pupsi Cola.*

---

# Creative Writing

Name _____

You have just opened a restaurant for children called **Yummies for the Tummies.** All of the food is prepared with ingredients that children love.

Create a menu. Write the name of each item and a short description. Be clever! **Example:** Frankfurterstein—a monster of a hot dog

### YUMMIES FOR THE TUMMIES
**MAIN DISHES**

*Answers will vary.*

**SIDE ORDERS**

**DESSERTS**

**DRINKS**

**Make Someone Smile**
Write a question for the riddle.

Question: _____

_____

Answer:  *So that you can have your cake and eat it, too!*

---

# Creative Writing

Name _____

**The good news is:** You are in the world's largest toy store—Toys-R-4-U.
**The bad news is:** It is nighttime and the workers locked you inside by mistake.

## TOYS TOYS TOYS TOYS TOYS TOYS

Complete your adventure by filling in the blanks with very descriptive words.

I couldn't believe *Answers will vary* . At first, I tried to

open the _____ doors, but I soon discovered that they would

be locked until _____ . So I decided that I might as well enjoy

my _____ . I walked down the _____ row and

saw a lot of _____ games. I really liked the game called

_____ because _____ . Next,

I _____ down the _____ . row.

Here I was _____ to see _____ robots. They

could do almost anything—even _____ ! I kept

on _____ until I suddenly found myself standing face-to-face

with a giant _____ . I couldn't believe it when

_____ . Finally, I came to the outdoor toys

where there were many different kinds of _____.I couldn't stop

laughing because _____ . Then, I heard a

_____ noise. I realized that this _____ store was

opening. I casually walked toward the front door, looked _____

at a clerk, and said, " _____ ."

**Make Someone Smile**
Complete the joke.

**The good news is:** You've just won a $1,000 shopping spree in a toy store.

**The bad news is:** _____

---

# Creative Writing

Name _____

You are the manager of Percival's Peculiar Pet Shop. The pets are so unusual that it is necessary to give extra information about each one. So that you don't have to keep repeating yourself, you've decided to place a sign near each pet.

Make a sign for four of the most peculiar animals. Include the type of animal, its name, where it was born, and what traits make it so unusual.

*Answers will vary.*

**Make Someone Smile**
Write an answer for the riddle.

Question: What do you get when you cross a crocodile with a gorilla?

Answer: _____

_____

---

113  IF8784 Second Grade in Review

## Creative Writing

Name _____

You are an editor of a large book company. Your job is to create snappy titles for new books.

Read the short summary for each book. Then write titles that will get the shoppers' attention so that they will want to buy each one.

*Answers will vary.*

For many years, Dr. Iva Lightfoot worked very hard to develop an antigravity formula. On the day that she finally was successful, her dog unknowingly drank the mixture.

_____

Minnie, a tiny seven-year-old, visited a rocket launch center. She wandered away from her parents and walked into a rocket ready for lift-off. Its destination was the moon. The rocket launched with her in it!

_____

The second grade class was having recess on the school playground. Suddenly, a huge UFO landed in the middle of the baseball diamond, and out walked some very strange visitors.

**Make Someone Smile**
Carefully read the author's name. Then write a funny title for the book.

| | | |
|---|---|---|
| by Belle E. Button | by Dan D. Lion | by Char Lee Horse |

Page 44

---

## Creative Writing

Name _____

The city zoo needs some improvements. Ms. Annie Mulluver, the manager, has asked interested people to write letters on how to improve it. You have some fantastic, new ideas. Write about them in the letter below.

Dear _____ *Answers will vary.*

_____
_____
_____
_____
_____
_____

_____ ,

**Make Someone Smile**
The animals have ideas about zoo improvements, too. Finish their statements.

I'm not *lyin'* . . .                    I can't *bear* to see

_____                    _____

Don't *monkey* around.

Page 45

---

## Creative Writing

Name _____

Choose a title. Then write a story that is out-of-this-world. Illustrate your story last.

**Titles**

My Teacher, the Alien
My Summer Vacation on Mars
What the Man on the Moon Is Really Like

Learning Proper Alien Manners
The Moon's Amusement Park

*Answers will vary.*

_____
_____
_____
_____
_____
_____
_____
_____

**Make Someone Smile**
Write an answer for the riddle.

**Question:** How would you shake hands with a six-armed Martian?

Answer: _____

Page 46

---

## Creative Writing

Name _____

The Sleepyhead

| mmrph... Time for school... | brush. brush. brush. clean those teeth... | HAND LOTION!?!! BLEECGH! |

Make a cartoon strip about something funny that happened to you or to someone in your family. Name your cartoon strip in the first box. Then use the rest of the boxes to draw your cartoon.

**Remember:** To show someone talking use ...

To show someone thinking use ...

| 1. *Answers will vary.* | 2. |
|---|---|
| 3. | 4. |
| 5. | 6. |
| 7. | 8. |

Page 47

---

## Creative Writing

Name _____

Before Miss Teree writes a story, she thinks really hard about her subject. Then she lists any words that relate to the story. This is called **brainstorming**.

Read each story idea. Then list any words that relate. When you are finished use another piece of paper to write a story using one of these titles and the words you listed.

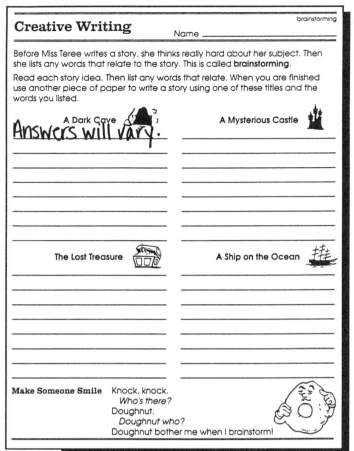

A Dark Cave

Answers will vary.

A Mysterious Castle

The Lost Treasure

A Ship on the Ocean

**Make Someone Smile**    Knock, knock.
*Who's there?*
Doughnut.
*Doughnut who?*
Doughnut bother me when I brainstorm!

Page 48

---

## Creative Writing

Name _____

Oh, no! Suddenly you've become invisible! What caused this? What things will you do now that you are invisible? How long will this last?

First, create a title for your story. Next, brainstorm and list words and ideas that will help you write your story. Then, create an interesting tale.

_____
(title)

Answers will vary.

**Make Someone Smile**
Write a question for the riddle:

Question: _____

Answer: *Evaporated milk and chocolate chip cookies*

Page 49

---

## Creative Writing

Name _____

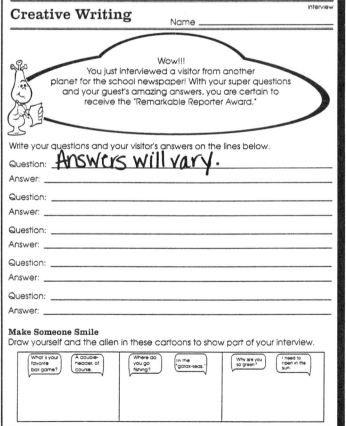

Wow!!!
You just interviewed a visitor from another planet for the school newspaper! With your super questions and your guest's amazing answers, you are certain to receive the "Remarkable Reporter Award."

Write your questions and your visitor's answers on the lines below.

Question: Answers will vary.

Answer: _____

Question: _____

Answer: _____

Question: _____

Answer: _____

Question: _____

Answer: _____

Question: _____

Answer: _____

**Make Someone Smile**
Draw yourself and the alien in these cartoons to show part of your interview.

| What's your favorite ball game? | A double-header, of course. | Where do you go fishing? | In the "galax-seas." | Why are you so green? | I need to ripen in the sun. |
|---|---|---|---|---|---|

Page 50

---

## Creative Writing

Name _____

Create a story to go with the ending sentence. Make sure that it blends smoothly into the ending.

Answers will vary.

. . . And that is the real reason that the chicken crossed the road!

**Make Someone Smile**
Write something funny that your chicken might say.

Page 51

---

## Creative Writing

Name _____

Create an ending to this spooky tale.

One dark and creepy night my friend Tiny and I slowly walked toward the rickety, old, wooden house at the end of the block. We tiptoed up the front walk as silently as possible. Tiny gently pushed the doorbell, but nothing happened. So he reached for the rusty doorknob and carefully turned it. The huge door creaked, squeaked, and finally opened. We stepped cautiously inside, and . . .

*Answers will vary.*

_____

_____

_____

_____

_____

_____

_____

_____

_____

_____

**Make Someone Smile:** Draw/color the characters for this cartoon.

---

## Creative Writing

Name _____

Choose words from each list of rhyming words to help you write a short poem. Draw a picture to go with each one.

bat, cat, chat, fat, flat, hat, pat, mat, rat, sat

*Answers will vary.*

_____

_____

_____

bean, clean, green, keen, lean, mean, queen, scene, screen, seen

_____

_____

_____

_____

deal, eel, feel, heel, kneel, meal, peel, real, reel, seal, squeal, steal, wheel

_____

_____

_____

_____

boat, coat, float, goat, moat, note, oat, throat, vote, wrote

_____

_____

_____

_____

**Make Someone Smile:** Write a funny, rhyming poem about yourself.

_____

_____

---

## Math

Name _____

Add the numbers in the glasses. Write the answers on the noses. Color the noses of the four largest answers.

5 + 6 = 11  
color 9 + 8 = 17  
5 + 1 = 6  
color 9 + 7 = 16

7 + 2 = 9  
3 + 3 = 6  
color 9 + 9 = 18  
2 + 9 = 11

color 8 + 8 = 16  
4 + 5 = 9  
6 + 0 = 6  
3 + 4 = 7

**Calculator Calisthenics**

Question: What was wrong with the girl who strained her eyes in the sun?

[ + ] the answers in each of the 4 colored noses

[ x ] five

[ = ] (Flip the calculator over.)

Answer: She was __see__ sick.

---

## Math

Name _____

Add the number on each can of pop to the number indicated by the code. Write the sum on the top of each can.

**Code**
1, 2, 3, 4, 5, 6, 7, 8, 9, 10

**Calculator Calisthenics**

Question: What kind of pop can't be poured from a can?

Enter: seventeen

[ x ] 1,000

[ + ] 700

[ + ] 7

[ = ] (Flip the calculator over.)

Answer: __lolli__ pop

---

Name _____

Howdy, partner! Write the answer to each problem in the boot. In each row across, color the boots with the same answer a matching color.

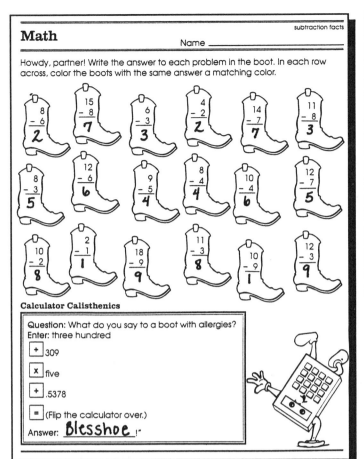

**Calculator Calisthenics**

Question: What do you say to a boot with allergies?
Enter: three hundred
+ 309
x five
+ .5378
= (Flip the calculator over.)
Answer: **Blesshoe** !"

Page 56

---

Name _____

Make the ghosts that have problems with wrong answers disappear by crossing them out.

**Calculator Calisthenics**

Question: What do you call a group of injured ghosts?
Enter: one thousand
x 1,000
x five
+ eight thousand
+ 8
= (Flip the calculator over.)
Answer: A bunch of **booboos**

Page 57

---

Name _____

Use the chart to help you write each problem. Then write each answer.

| Roman Numeral Chart | | | | | | | | |
|---|---|---|---|---|---|---|---|---|
| 1 | 2 | 3 | 4 | 5 | 6 | 7 | 8 | 9 |
| I | II | III | IV | V | VI | VII | VIII | IX |

Example:
V = 5
II = 2
+ IX = 9

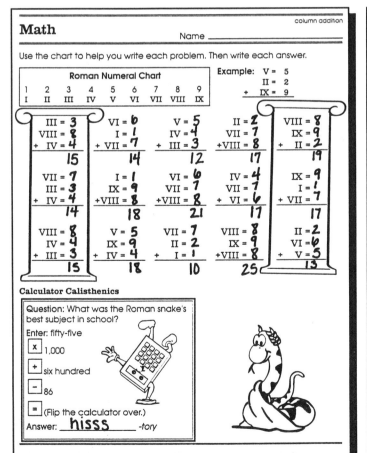

III = 3, VIII = 8, + IV = 4 → 15
VI = 6, I = 1, + VII = 7 → 14
V = 5, IV = 4, + III = 3 → 12
II = 2, VII = 7, +VIII = 8 → 17
VIII = 8, IX = 9, + II = 2 → 19

VII = 7, III = 3, + IV = 4 → 14
I = 1, IX = 9, +VIII = 8 → 18
VI = 6, VII = 7, +VIII = 8 → 21
IV = 4, VII = 7, + VI = 6 → 17
IX = 9, I = 1, + VII = 7 → 17

VIII = 8, IV = 4, + III = 3 → 15
V = 5, IX = 9, + IV = 4 → 18
VII = 7, II = 2, + I = 1 → 10
VIII = 8, IX = 9, +VIII = 8 → 25
II = 2, VI = 6, + V = 5 → 13

**Calculator Calisthenics**

Question: What was the Roman snake's best subject in school?
Enter: fifty-five
x 1,000
+ six hundred
- 86
= (Flip the calculator over.)
Answer: **hisss** -tory

Page 58

---

Name _____

Jack and the giant were always comparing beanstalks. The height of Jack's beanstalk is listed first on each leaf. It is followed by the height of the giant's beanstalk. Draw the correct symbol between the numbers in each pair.

| < | = | > |
|---|---|---|
| less than | equal | greater than |

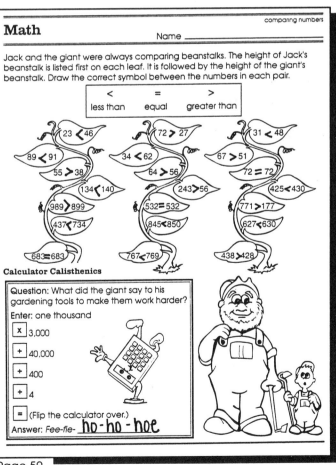

23 < 46    72 > 27    31 < 48
89 < 91    34 < 62    67 > 51
55 > 38    64 > 56    72 = 72
134 < 140    243 > 56    425 < 430
989 > 899    532 = 532    771 > 177
437 < 734    845 < 850    627 < 630
683 = 683    767 < 769    438 > 428

**Calculator Calisthenics**

Question: What did the giant say to his gardening tools to make them work harder?
Enter: one thousand
x 3,000
+ 40,000
+ 400
+ 4
= (Flip the calculator over.)
Answer: Fee-fie- **ho-ho-hoe**

Page 59

---

## Page 60

Help each fish add its two scores for the video game "Escaping Captain Hook."

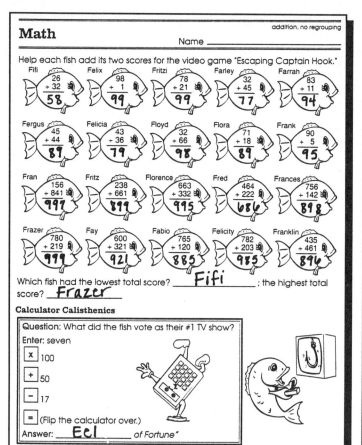

Fifi: 26 + 58 = 58... 26 + 32 = 58
Felix: 98 + 1 = 99
Fritzi: 78 + 21 = 99
Farley: 32 + 45 = 77
Farrah: 83 + 11 = 94

Fergus: 45 + 44 = 89
Felicia: 43 + 36 = 79
Floyd: 32 + 66 = 98
Flora: 71 + 18 = 89
Frank: 90 + 5 = 95

Fran: 156 + 841 = 997
Fritz: 238 + 661 = 899
Florence: 663 + 332 = 995
Fred: 464 + 222 = 686
Frances: 756 + 142 = 898

Frazer: 780 + 219 = 999
Fay: 600 + 321 = 921
Fabio: 765 + 120 = 885
Felicity: 782 + 203 = 985
Franklin: 435 + 461 = 896

Which fish had the lowest total score? **Fifi** ; the highest total score? **Frazer**

**Calculator Calisthenics**

Question: What did the fish vote as their #1 TV show?

Enter: seven

☒ 100
➕ 50
➖ 17
🟰 (Flip the calculator over.)

Answer: **Eel** of Fortune"

## Page 61

Use the Word Bank to complete the crossword puzzle.

| Word Bank | | |
|---|---|---|
| one | four | seven |
| two | five | eight |
| three | six | nine |

**Across**
1. The number in the tens place in 549
3. 800 + 30 + 7 = 83 _____
6. 3 ones = _____

**Down**
2. 600 + 10 + 5 = 6 _____ 5
3. 6 hundreds = _____ 00
4. The number in the hundreds place in 873
5. 50 = _____ tens

Crossword: four / seven / six / five / three

**Calculator Calisthenics**

Question: What did the teacher say to the cross word to make it stop complaining?

Enter: forty-four

☒ one hundred
➕ fifty
➖ five
🟰 (Flip the calculator over.)

Answer: " **Shhh** !"

## Page 62

Help Mortimer Mouse escape the claws of Toby Tomcat by showing him the correct path home. Add the numbers of the first problem. Then draw a line from the answer to the problem that begins with that same number. Continue adding and drawing lines until you reach Mortimer's hole. Then solve the other problems.

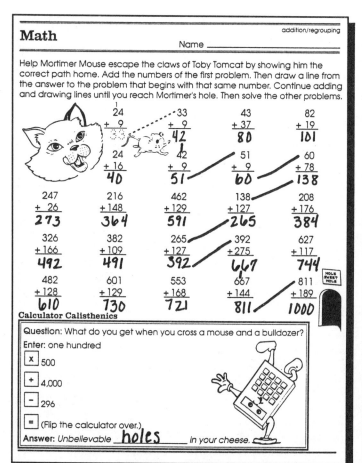

24 + 9 = 33
33 + 9 = 42
43 + 37 = 80
82 + 19 = 101

24 + 16 = 40
42 + 9 = 51
51 + 9 = 60
60 + 78 = 138

247 + 26 = 273
216 + 148 = 364
462 + 129 = 591
138 + 127 = 265
208 + 176 = 384

326 + 166 = 492
382 + 109 = 491
265 + 127 = 392
392 + 275 = 667
627 + 117 = 744

482 + 128 = 610
601 + 129 = 730
553 + 168 = 721
667 + 144 = 811
811 + 189 = 1000

**Calculator Calisthenics**

Question: What do you get when you cross a mouse and a bulldozer?

Enter: one hundred

☒ 500
➕ 4,000
➖ 296
🟰 (Flip the calculator over.)

Answer: Unbelievable **holes** in your cheese.

## Page 63

Tucker Turtle had a big problem. He walked in his sleep—backwards! Subtract the distance he walked backwards from the distance he walked forward each day.

25 forward − 12 backwards = 13
46 − 23 = 23
83 − 40 = 43
78 − 17 = 61
99 − 25 = 74

36 − 21 = 15
64 − 14 = 50
56 − 11 = 45
80 − 20 = 60
77 − 14 = 63

383 − 252 = 131
768 − 631 = 137
976 − 852 = 124
387 − 306 = 81
271 − 131 = 140

845 − 432 = 413
662 − 552 = 110
406 − 101 = 305
592 − 482 = 110
687 − 616 = 71

367 − 255 = 112
546 − 135 = 411
378 − 251 = 127
989 − 887 = 102
800 − 200 = 600

**Calculator Calisthenics:**

Question: Where did Tucker Turtle finally go for "repairs"?

Enter: seventy

☒ 1,000
➕ 7,400
➖ fifty-five
🟰 (Flip the calculator over.)

Answer: To the **shell** station

# Math

Name _____

Bloodsworth Bloodhound could sense the scent of cents so well that the U.S. Treasury Department put him in charge of counting money. How much money did he sniff in each bank? Write the answer.

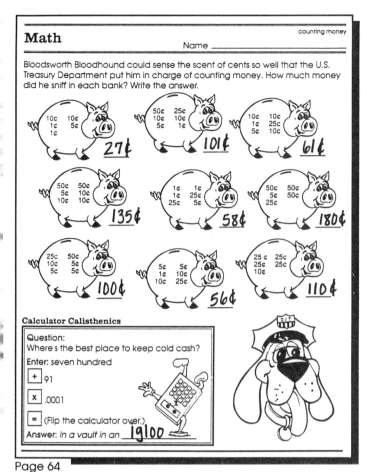

27¢  101¢  61¢

135¢  58¢  180¢

100¢  56¢  110¢

**Calculator Calisthenics**

Question:
Where's the best place to keep cold cash?
Enter: seven hundred

[+] 91

[x] .0001

[=] (Flip the calculator over.)

Answer: In a vault in an __19100__

---

# Math

Name _____

Every morning Grandfather Cluck wakes up Old MacDonald's family at a different time. Write each time. Then, make each clock into the face of someone in Old MacDonald's family.

**4:00** a.m.  **6:25** a.m.  **3:10** a.m.

**5:15** a.m.  **5:40** a.m.  **4:05** a.m.

**6:55** a.m.  **3:35** a.m.  **12:00** a.m.

**Calculator Calisthenics**

Question: Why did Mrs. Cluck wear a watch?
Enter: one hundred

[−] 41

[x] 100

[+] 93

[=] (Flip the calculator over.)

Answer: So she could find **eggs** -tra time to read "The Little Red Hen."

---

# Math

Name _____

Freddie Frog plays hopscotch every day, but he only hops on boxes with odd numbers. Draw an **X** on all of the boxes on which Freddie would jump.

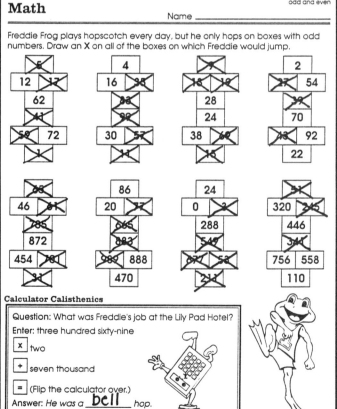

**Calculator Calisthenics**

Question: What was Freddie's job at the Lily Pad Hotel?
Enter: three hundred sixty-nine

[x] two

[+] seven thousand

[=] (Flip the calculator over.)

Answer: He was a __bell__ hop.

---

# Math

Name _____

The Elastic Man can bend his body in many ways. Carefully look at the diagram and use an inch ruler to draw him the correct number of inches on a large sheet of paper. Then add details to your picture for fun!

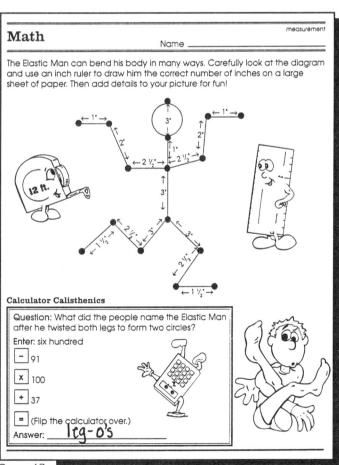

**Calculator Calisthenics**

Question: What did the people name the Elastic Man after he twisted both legs to form two circles?
Enter: six hundred

[−] 91

[x] 100

[+] 37

[=] (Flip the calculator over.)

Answer: __leg-o's__

© Instructional Fair, Inc.   IF8784 Second Grade in Review

Something's shaping up, and it's driving everyone buggy! First, draw a line from each geometric shape to its name.

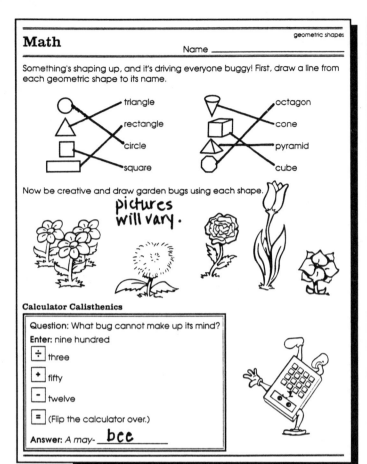

- triangle
- rectangle
- circle
- square

- octagon
- cone
- pyramid
- cube

Now be creative and draw garden bugs using each shape.

pictures will vary.

### Calculator Calisthenics

Question: What bug cannot make up its mind?

Enter: nine hundred

- ÷ three
- + fifty
- − twelve
- = (Flip the calculator over.)

Answer: A may- **bee**

Page 68

---

Use the Word Bank to write the missing letters of each math word.

| Word Bank | | | |
|---|---|---|---|
| ace | end | rod | rap |
| vision | sub | group | action |
| apes | cent | if | tip |

1. ___**sub**___ tract (underwater ship)
2. g___**rap**___h (kind of music)
3. di___**vision**___ (eyesight)
4. ___**cent**___imeter (a penny)
5. fr___**action**___ (movement)
6. add___**end**___ (antonym of "beginning")
7. sh___**apes**___ (monkeys)
8. p___**rod**___uct (fishing pole)
9. d___**if**___ference (whether)
10. mul___**tip**___lication (knock over)
11. pl___**ace**___ value (playing card—one)
12. re___**group**___ (a team)

### Calculator Calisthenics

Question: What letters make farm animals feel like dancing?

Enter: thirteen

- + 1,300
- × .0001
- = (Flip the calculator over.)

Answer: **E·1·E·1·0**

Page 69

---

Eight football teams have just completed their season. Each team played eight games. Use this pictograph to answer the questions below.

**Season Wins**          ⊘ = 1 win

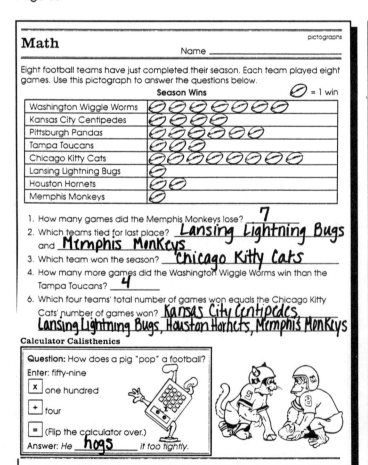

| Washington Wiggle Worms | ⊘⊘⊘⊘⊘⊘⊘ |
| Kansas City Centipedes | ⊘⊘⊘⊘ |
| Pittsburgh Pandas | ⊘⊘⊘⊘⊘ |
| Tampa Toucans | ⊘⊘⊘ |
| Chicago Kitty Cats | ⊘⊘⊘⊘⊘⊘⊘⊘ |
| Lansing Lightning Bugs | ⊘ |
| Houston Hornets | ⊘⊘ |
| Memphis Monkeys | ⊘ |

1. How many games did the Memphis Monkeys lose? **7**
2. Which teams tied for last place? **Lansing Lightning Bugs** and **Memphis Monkeys**
3. Which team won the season? **Chicago Kitty Cats**
4. How many more games did the Washington Wiggle Worms win than the Tampa Toucans? **4**
6. Which four teams' total number of games won equals the Chicago Kitty Cats' number of games won? **Kansas City Centipedes, Lansing Lightning Bugs, Houston Hornets, Memphis Monkeys**

### Calculator Calisthenics

Question: How does a pig "pop" a football?

Enter: fifty-nine

- × one hundred
- + four
- = (Flip the calculator over.)

Answer: He **hogs** it too tightly.

Page 70

---

Thomas Sayva Turkey decided to offer diners new choices for Thanksgiving dinner. Chart the following choices on the bar graph. Color each bar a different color.

**Choices**

- 15 chose hamburgers
- 10 chose hot dogs
- 30 chose chicken
- 25 chose steak
- 5 chose perch
- 15 chose ham

**New Thanksgiving Dinners**

Hot Dogs / Steak / Chicken / Ham / Perch / Hamburgers
0 5 10 15 20 25 30 35

Use the graph to answer the questions.

1. How many people altogether tried new Thanksgiving dinners? **100**
2. Which was the favorite new meal? **chicken**
3. Which new meal did they choose the least? **perch**
4. Which was a more popular choice—hamburgers or hot dogs? **hamburgers**
5. How many more people chose ham than perch? **10**
6. Who should be more worried now—Porky Pig or Chicken Little? **Chicken Little**
7. Which of the meals would be your first choice? **Answers will vary.**

### Calculator Calisthenics

Question: How can you tell when Thomas is hungry?

Enter: 5,000

- × 1,000
- + 378,809
- = (Flip the calculator over.)

Answer: By the way he **gobbles** his food.

Page 71

---

## Social Studies

Name _____

Follow the directions to find the hidden treasures and surprises. Color the footsteps as you go.

### Directions

1. Begin at the pyramid. Walk 3 steps east, 1 step south, and 2 steps southeast. Draw a snake on the nearby rock to remind you to beware of the snake pit.

2. Go 2 steps directly north of the rock and 1 step east. Draw a golden necklace on this rock to show you have discovered the queen's jewelry.

3. Move 3 steps south of the jewelry. Then walk 2 steps west. Continue by going 3 steps northwest and 2 steps south. Draw a mummy on the rock. You have now found the pharoah and his queen.

4. Next, travel 2 steps northwest and 2 steps north. You are now back to the pyramid.

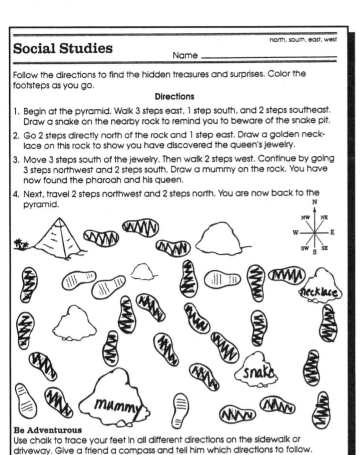

**Be Adventurous**
Use chalk to trace your feet in all different directions on the sidewalk or driveway. Give a friend a compass and tell him which directions to follow.

Page 72

---

## Social Studies

Name _____

Complete the pirate's treasure map by following the directions and using these symbols:

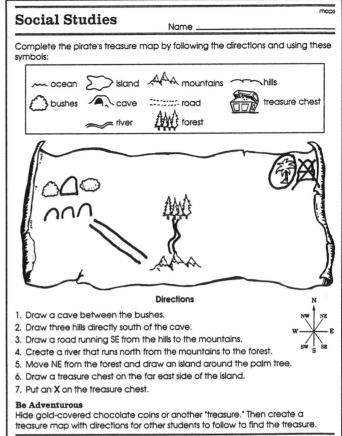

### Directions

1. Draw a cave between the bushes.
2. Draw three hills directly south of the cave.
3. Draw a road running SE from the hills to the mountains.
4. Create a river that runs north from the mountains to the forest.
5. Move NE from the forest and draw an island around the palm tree.
6. Draw a treasure chest on the far east side of the island.
7. Put an X on the treasure chest.

**Be Adventurous**
Hide gold-covered chocolate coins or another "treasure." Then create a treasure map with directions for other students to follow to find the treasure.

Page 73

---

## Social Studies

Name _____

Use the clues to label the rooms on the castle's blueprints by writing the number of each room in the proper area.

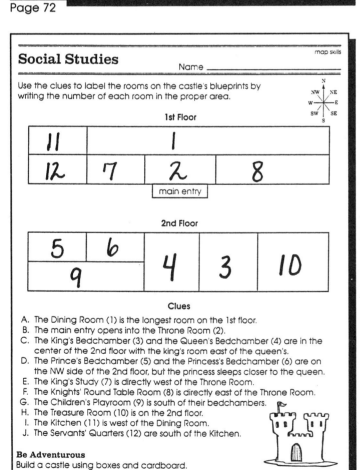

### Clues

A. The Dining Room (1) is the longest room on the 1st floor.
B. The main entry opens into the Throne Room (2).
C. The King's Bedchamber (3) and the Queen's Bedchamber (4) are in the center of the 2nd floor with the king's room east of the queen's.
D. The Prince's Bedchamber (5) and the Princess's Bedchamber (6) are on the NW side of the 2nd floor, but the princess sleeps closer to the queen.
E. The King's Study (7) is directly west of the Throne Room.
F. The Knights' Round Table Room (8) is directly east of the Throne Room.
G. The Children's Playroom (9) is south of their bedchambers.
H. The Treasure Room (10) is on the 2nd floor.
I. The Kitchen (11) is west of the Dining Room.
J. The Servants' Quarters (12) are south of the Kitchen.

**Be Adventurous**
Build a castle using boxes and cardboard.

Page 74

---

## Social Studies

Name _____

Use the clues to complete the names of the world's continents and oceans.

**Across:**
2. thick string or twine
3. leave it _____ is
5. opposite of in
7. a banana, ___ apple
8. another name for dad
9. a Native American

**Down:**
1. opposite of south
4. not them, but _____
6. a hardworking insect

**Be Adventurous**
Locate the continents and oceans on a world map. If possible, use a marker to draw them on an old playground ball.

Page 75

---

## Page 76

The United States has many interesting places to visit. Circle the names of a few hidden below. Look → or ↓ .

**Word Bank**

| | | |
|---|---|---|
| Liberty Bell | Yellowstone National Park | Hollywood |
| Lincoln Memorial | Statue of Liberty | White House |
| Alamo | Cape Canaveral | Mount Rushmore |
| Disney World | U.S.S. Arizona Memorial | Grand Canyon |

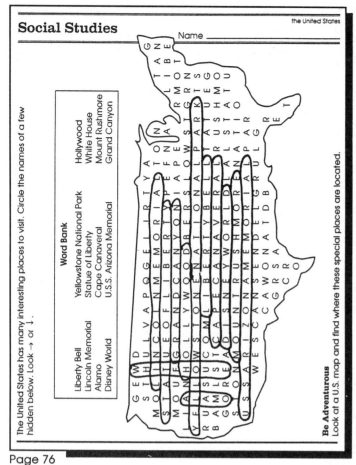

**Be Adventurous**
Look at a U.S. map and find where these special places are located.

---

## Page 77

Every worker needs specific things to help him do his job well. After each career are listed different things which that worker may need. Put an X on the one that's incorrect. Then, write something which that worker might need that rhymes with the word you crossed out.

1. teacher— ~~cook~~   yardstick   chalk    **book**
2. dentist— crown   toothbrush   ~~pill~~    **drill**
3. cook— pots   pans   ~~glove~~    **stove**
4. carpenter— hammer   ~~claws~~   nails    **saw**
5. artist— paint   ~~mush~~   canvas    **brush**
6. actor— ~~cage~~   costumes   makeup    **stage**
7. astronaut— ~~socket~~   helmet   suit    **rocket**
8. farmer— tractor   barn   ~~beads~~    **seeds**
9. writer— ~~hen~~   paper   typewriter    **pen**
10. florist— plants   ~~shower~~   soil    **flower**

**Be Adventurous**
Instead of playing "school," play "law office," "White House," "farm," or "hospital."

---

## Page 78

Unscramble the names of the holidays in the following months.

**January**
ewN reYas' yaD
**New Years' Day**

**February**
enalVtnie's aDy
**Valentines Day**

**March**
tS. rc'skitaP ayD
**St. Patrick's Day**

**April**
plriA oloFs' Dya
**April Fools' Day**

**May**
oilaMmer ayD
**Memorial Day**

**June**
glaF yDa
**Flag Day**

**July**
delnecnepned Dya
**Independence Day**

**August**

**September**
broLa aDy
**Labor Day**

**October**
llowneHae
**Halloween**

**November**
ggvilnksnahT
**Thanksgiving**

**December**
stirmsaCh
**Christmas**

**Be Adventurous**
See how many other holidays you can list for each month.

---

## Page 79

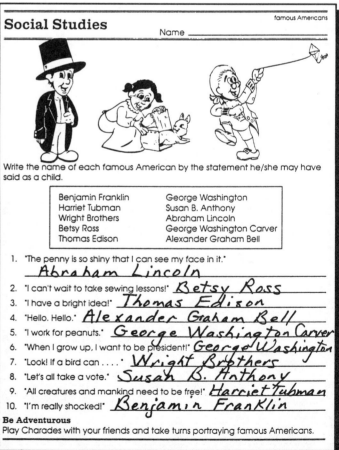

Write the name of each famous American by the statement he/she may have said as a child.

| | |
|---|---|
| Benjamin Franklin | George Washington |
| Harriet Tubman | Susan B. Anthony |
| Wright Brothers | Abraham Lincoln |
| Betsy Ross | George Washington Carver |
| Thomas Edison | Alexander Graham Bell |

1. "The penny is so shiny that I can see my face in it."   **Abraham Lincoln**
2. "I can't wait to take sewing lessons!"   **Betsy Ross**
3. "I have a bright idea!"   **Thomas Edison**
4. "Hello. Hello."   **Alexander Graham Bell**
5. "I work for peanuts."   **George Washington Carver**
6. "When I grow up, I want to be president!"   **George Washington**
7. "Look! If a bird can . . . ."   **Wright Brothers**
8. "Let's all take a vote."   **Susan B. Anthony**
9. "All creatures and mankind need to be free!"   **Harriet Tubman**
10. "I'm really shocked!"   **Benjamin Franklin**

**Be Adventurous**
Play Charades with your friends and take turns portraying famous Americans.

---

# Social Studies

Name _____

Look closely at each set of pictures. Number them in order.

**Be Adventurous**
Make cookies. Set up a stand and sell them. Use the money to buy something for your classroom.

---

# Social Studies

Name _____

Everyone has **needs** such as shelter, clothing, food, and love. We also have **wants**, which are things we would like to have but don't really need.

Cut out the puzzle pieces. When you put them together correctly you will have two puzzles. One will show **needs** and the other **wants**.

**Be Adventurous**
Make two lists of the things in your bedroom. One list will name things you needed and the other will list things you wanted. Which is bigger?

---

# Social Studies

Name _____

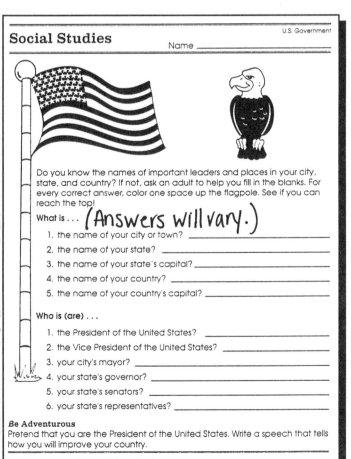

Do you know the names of important leaders and places in your city, state, and country? If not, ask an adult to help you fill in the blanks. For every correct answer, color one space up the flagpole. See if you can reach the top!

What is . . . *(Answers will vary.)*

1. the name of your city or town? _____
2. the name of your state? _____
3. the name of your state's capital? _____
4. the name of your country? _____
5. the name of your country's capital? _____

Who is (are) . . .

1. the President of the United States? _____
2. the Vice President of the United States? _____
3. your city's mayor? _____
4. your state's governor? _____
5. your state's senators? _____
6. your state's representatives? _____

**Be Adventurous**
Pretend that you are the President of the United States. Write a speech that tells how you will improve your country.

---

# Science

Name _____

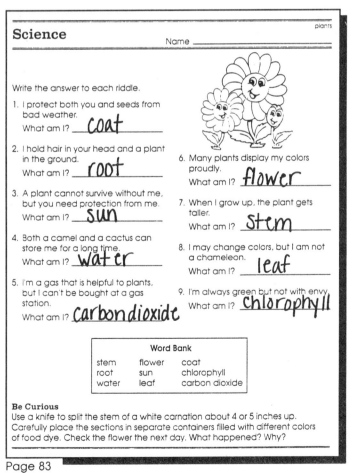

Write the answer to each riddle.

1. I protect both you and seeds from bad weather.
   What am I? __coat__

2. I hold hair in your head and a plant in the ground.
   What am I? __root__

3. A plant cannot survive without me, but you need protection from me.
   What am I? __sun__

4. Both a camel and a cactus can store me for a long time.
   What am I? __water__

5. I'm a gas that is helpful to plants, but I can't be bought at a gas station.
   What am I? __carbon dioxide__

6. Many plants display my colors proudly.
   What am I? __flower__

7. When I grow up, the plant gets taller.
   What am I? __stem__

8. I may change colors, but I am not a chameleon.
   What am I? __leaf__

9. I'm always green but not with envy.
   What am I? __chlorophyll__

| Word Bank | | |
|---|---|---|
| stem | flower | coat |
| root | sun | chlorophyll |
| water | leaf | carbon dioxide |

**Be Curious**
Use a knife to split the stem of a white carnation about 4 or 5 inches up. Carefully place the sections in separate containers filled with different colors of food dye. Check the flower the next day. What happened? Why?

---

 IF8784 Second Grade in Review

## Science

Name _____

**Endangered** animals may soon disappear from earth. That's what happened to dinosaurs, dodo birds, and passenger pigeons. They became **extinct**.

Write the letter that comes before each letter to decode the names of some endangered animals.

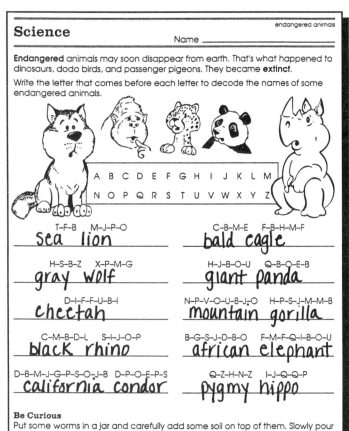

A B C D E F G H I J K L M
N O P Q R S T U V W X Y Z

T-F-B  M-J-P-O
sea lion

C-B-M-E  F-B-H-M-F
bald eagle

H-S-B-Z  X-P-M-G
gray wolf

H-J-B-O-U  Q-B-O-E-B
giant panda

D-I-F-F-U-B-I
cheetah

N-P-V-O-U-B-J-O  H-P-S-J-M-M-B
mountain gorilla

C-M-B-D-L  S-I-J-O-P
black rhino

B-G-S-J-D-B-O  F-M-F-Q-I-B-O-U
african elephant

D-B-M-J-G-P-S-O-J-B  D-P-O-E-P-S
california condor

Q-Z-H-N-Z  I-J-Q-Q-P
pygmy hippo

**Be Curious**
Put some worms in a jar and carefully add some soil on top of them. Slowly pour in a little water and watch the worms. What did they do? Why?

Page 84

---

## Science

Name _____

Write each animal name in the correct category.

| crocodile | canary | dog | sparrow | lizard |
|---|---|---|---|---|
| trout | toad | robin | tiger | shark |
| python | bear | guppy | salamander | newt |

**Mammals**
bear
dog
tiger

**Amphibians**
toad
salamander
newt

**Fish**
trout
shark
guppy

**Reptiles**
crocodile
python
lizard

**Birds**
robin
sparrow
canary

Imagine that two animals combined to form a new species. Which two categories would each of the following represent?

ostricheetah — bird — mammal
turtleopard — reptile — mammal
eelephant — fish — mammal
frogorilla — amphibian — mammal
pelicanteater — bird — mammal
kangarooster — mammal — bird
cardinalligator — bird — reptile
cobratuna — reptile — fish

**Be Curious**
Look for animal holes in a park or your yard. If you don't see any footprints, smooth some mud around the hole. Return the next day. What type of footprints do you see? If there are no footprints, could the hole belong to a snake?

Page 85

---

## Science

Name _____

Insects have compound eyes, two antennae, zero to four wings, six legs, and three body parts. Draw an **X** on each insect.

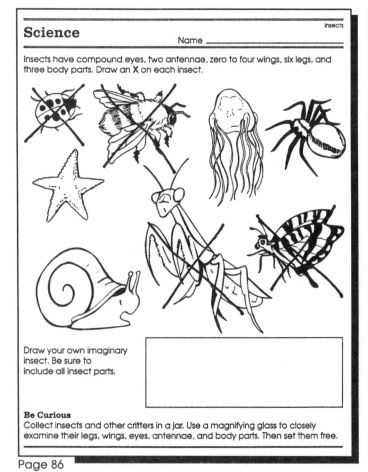

Draw your own imaginary insect. Be sure to include all insect parts.

**Be Curious**
Collect insects and other critters in a jar. Use a magnifying glass to closely examine their legs, wings, eyes, antennae, and body parts. Then set them free.

Page 86

---

## Science

Name _____

Solve each rebus to write the names of the planets.

| Earth | Mercury | Saturn |
|---|---|---|
| Jupiter | Neptune | Uranus |
| Mars | Pluto | Venus |

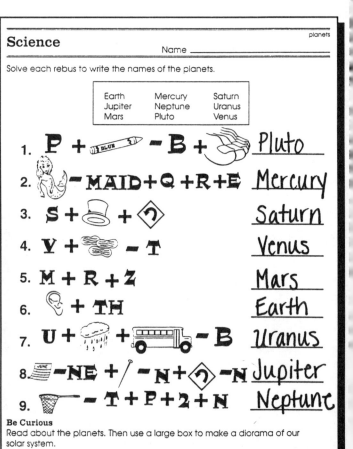

1. P + [crayon] BLUS – B + [shrimp]  Pluto
2. [mermaid] – MAID + Q + R + E  Mercury
3. S + [hat] + [diamond]  Saturn
4. V + [noodles] – T  Venus
5. M + R + Z  Mars
6. [ear] + TH  Earth
7. U + [rain] + [bus] – B  Uranus
8. [June calendar] – NE + / – N + [diamond] – N  Jupiter
9. [net] – T + P + 2 + N  Neptune

**Be Curious**
Read about the planets. Then use a large box to make a diorama of our solar system.

Page 87

---

## Page 88

Name _____

Find the hidden matter in the spiral and write each one in the correct category. Start at the center.

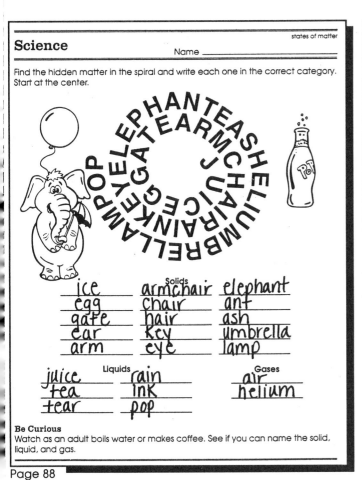

ELEPHANTEASHELLIUMCHAIRJUICE... POPELEPHANTEARMCHAIR... MELAMBRELLA... GATEARN... KEYEGATEARMCHAIR... AINKEG...

**Solids**
| | | |
|---|---|---|
| ice | armchair | elephant |
| egg | chair | ant |
| gate | hair | ash |
| ear | key | umbrella |
| arm | eye | lamp |

**Liquids**
| | |
|---|---|
| juice | rain |
| tea | ink |
| tear | pop |

**Gases**
air
helium

**Be Curious**
Watch as an adult boils water or makes coffee. See if you can name the solid, liquid, and gas.

---

## Page 89

Name _____

A meteorologist uses many weather words in a forecast. Underline the hidden word in each sentence. The first one is done for you.

| thunder | humid | foggy |
|---|---|---|
| snow | downpour | rainy |
| chilly | sunshine | gusty |

1. Put a cloth under the can.
2. As the rain falls down, pour what's collected onto the plant.
3. I can see the sun shine brightly through the window.
4. Get the umbrellas now!
5. In the thick fog, gypsy moths are hard to find.
6. With all this rain, you feel like a fish.
7. Warm weather makes me hum idiotic, silly songs.
8. In August you often need to sit near a cool fan.
9. With this chill, you might catch a cold.

Unscramble other weather words.
1. itlghnngi — lightning
2. laih — hail
3. ndaotor — tornado
4. ihrrcnaeu — hurricane
5. lirzzdab — blizzard

**Be Curious**
Use a can to collect rain or snow. See how long it takes to fill it to the top.

---

## Page 90

Name _____

Follow the directions to write the name of each dinosaur in the correct place on the grid.

Write . . .

| | | |
|---|---|---|
| **apatosaurus** in C2 | **trachodon** in A1 | **stegosaurus** in B3 |
| **triceratops** in A3 | **elasmosaurus** in C3 | **iguanodon** in A2 |
| **tyrannosaurus** in B1 | **pterosaur** in B2 | **brachiosaurus** in C1 |
| **allosaurus** in D3 | **protoceratops** in D1 | **ankylosaurus** in D2 |

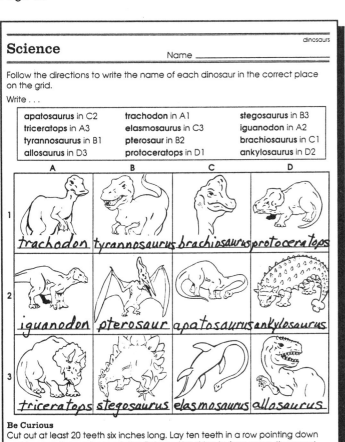

| | A | B | C | D |
|---|---|---|---|---|
| 1 | trachodon | tyrannosaurus | brachiosaurus | protoceratops |
| 2 | iguanodon | pterosaur | apatosaurus | ankylosaurus |
| 3 | triceratops | stegosaurus | elasmosaurus | allosaurus |

**Be Curious**
Cut out at least 20 teeth six inches long. Lay ten teeth in a row pointing down and ten pointing up beneath the first row. Use string to form a mouth around the teeth. Imagine a tyrannosaurus coming to eat you for dinner.

---

## Page 91

Name _____

Put an **X** on the word that does **not** make sense in the sentence. Write the word that should be in the sentence. **Hint:** It rhymes with the crossed-out word.

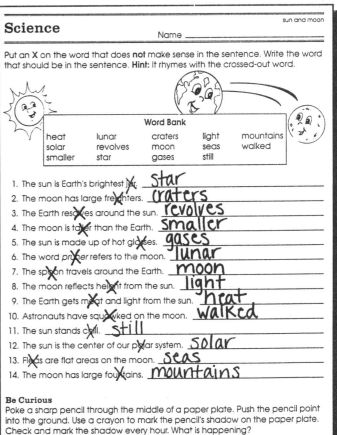

**Word Bank**
| | | | | |
|---|---|---|---|---|
| heat | lunar | craters | light | mountains |
| solar | revolves | moon | seas | walked |
| smaller | star | gases | still | |

1. The sun is Earth's brightest jar. — star
2. The moon has large freighters. — craters
3. The Earth resolves around the sun. — revolves
4. The moon is taller than the Earth. — smaller
5. The sun is made up of hot glasses. — gases
6. The word prayer refers to the moon. — lunar
7. The spoon travels around the Earth. — moon
8. The moon reflects height from the sun. — light
9. The Earth gets meat and light from the sun. — heat
10. Astronauts have squawked on the moon. — walked
11. The sun stands chill. — still
12. The sun is the center of our polar system. — solar
13. Fleas are flat areas on the moon. — seas
14. The moon has large fountains. — mountains

**Be Curious**
Poke a sharp pencil through the middle of a paper plate. Push the pencil point into the ground. Use a crayon to mark the pencil's shadow on the paper plate. Check and mark the shadow every hour. What is happening?

---

# Science

Name _____

Draw the correct symbol for each habitat by each animal.

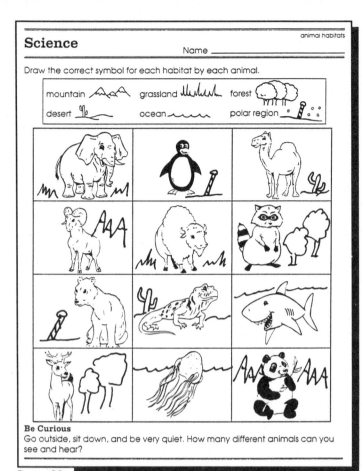

**Be Curious**
Go outside, sit down, and be very quiet. How many different animals can you see and hear?

Page 92

---

# Science

Name _____

Be an energizer! Put the letters in correct numerical order to form words about energy. Then draw lines to match the words to their meanings.

```
5 4 2 1 6 3 8 7
t c r f i i n o
friction
```
a. form of energy used to run machines

```
4 2 5 1 3
h i t l g
light
```
b. object burned to give heat

```
5 2 1 3 4
d o s u n
sound
```
c. a form of energy that you can see

```
11 5 9 6 4 2 1 3 10 8 7
y t i r c l e e t a i
electricity
```
d. made when an object blocks light

```
2 3 5 1 4 6
h a o s d w
shadow
```
e. a form of energy that you can hear

```
4 2 1 3
l u f e
fuel
```
f. rubbing two objects together

**Be Curious**
In a quiet room, hold a paper cup to one ear and plug the other ear with a finger. What do you hear? Repeat using a glass. What do you hear now? Are the sounds you hear through the paper cup the same as the sounds you hear through the glass?

Page 93

---

# Health

Name _____

Draw how your face would look in each situation. **Answers will vary.**

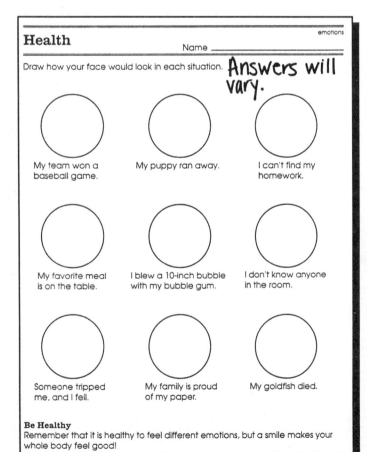

My team won a baseball game.

My puppy ran away.

I can't find my homework.

My favorite meal is on the table.

I blew a 10-inch bubble with my bubble gum.

I don't know anyone in the room.

Someone tripped me, and I fell.

My family is proud of my paper.

My goldfish died.

**Be Healthy**
Remember that it is healthy to feel different emotions, but a smile makes your whole body feel good!

Page 94

---

# Health

Name _____

Fill in the missing letter(s) in the foods in each group.

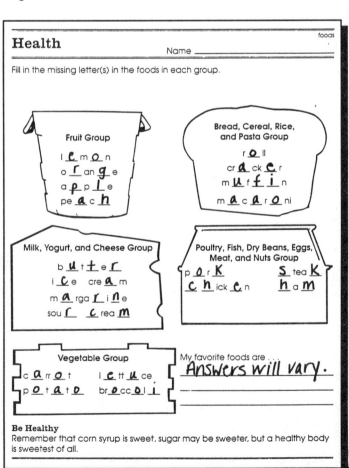

**Fruit Group**
l e m o n
o r a n g e
a p p l e
pe a c h

**Bread, Cereal, Rice, and Pasta Group**
r o ll
cr a ck e r
m u f f i n
m a c a r o ni

**Milk, Yogurt, and Cheese Group**
b u t t e r
i c e cre a m
m a rga r i n e
sou r c rea m

**Poultry, Fish, Dry Beans, Eggs, Meat, and Nuts Group**
p o r K    S tea K
c h ick e n    h a m

**Vegetable Group**
c a rr o t    l e tt u ce
p o t a t o    br o cc o l i

My favorite foods are . . .
**Answers will vary.**

**Be Healthy**
Remember that corn syrup is sweet, sugar may be sweeter, but a healthy body is sweetest of all.

Page 95

---

Exercise is important for a healthy body. Write the sport or activity on the line that matches each picture.

**Word Bank**

| jogging | soccer | baseball | football |
|---------|--------|----------|----------|
| jumping | hockey | tennis | swimming |
| roller blading | | | |

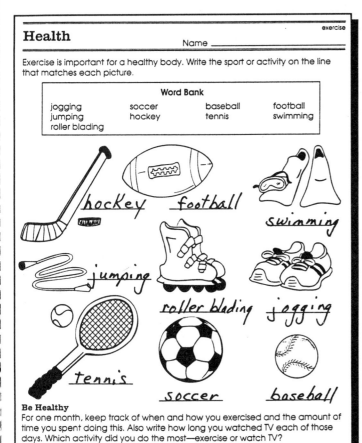

**Be Healthy**
For one month, keep track of when and how you exercised and the amount of time you spent doing this. Also write how long you watched TV each of those days. Which activity did you do the most—exercise or watch TV?

Page 96

---

Fill in the missing letters in each sentence to complete information about your body.

1. Your hea **r** t brings foo **d** and oxyg **e** n to your cells.
2. Sto **m** ach juices br **e** ak dow **n** fo **o** d.
3. B **o** nes help give your bod **y** sh **a** pe.
4. Lu **n** gs help you brea **t** he.
5. Ski **n** prot **e** cts your insid **e** org **a** ns.
6. Your bra **i** n contro **l** s almost ever **y** thi **n** g your body doe **s** .
7. Most of your hai **r** is not l **i** vi **n** g.
8. Bone **s** are made up of livi **n** g cell **s** .
9. Your skelet **o** n has 206 b **o** nes.
10. Saliv **a** helps you swal **l** ow and diges **t** food.
11. Muscl **e** s help your bod **y** move.
12. The hea **r** t is your stron **g** est mus **c** le.
13. Kee **p** clea **n** , exe **r** cise, ea **t** good **f** ood, and get pl **e** nty of res **t** to sta **y** heal **t** hy.

**Be Healthy**
Make a list of your good health habits. Then make a list of your bad health habits. Which list is longer? How can you improve?

Page 97

---

Play "Teeth Trivia." Uncover facts about teeth by reading the scrambled words in a mirror. Then write the words correctly on the lines.

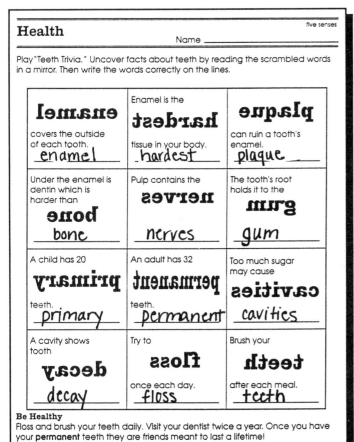

| enamel | hardest | plaque |
|--------|---------|--------|
| covers the outside of each tooth. enamel | Enamel is the hardest tissue in your body. hardest | can ruin a tooth's enamel. plaque |
| Under the enamel is dentin which is harder than bone. bone | Pulp contains the nerves. nerves | The tooth's root holds it to the gum. gum |
| A child has 20 primary teeth. primary | An adult has 32 permanent teeth. permanent | Too much sugar may cause cavities. cavities |
| A cavity shows tooth decay. decay | Try to floss once each day. floss | Brush your teeth after each meal. teeth |

**Be Healthy**
Floss and brush your teeth daily. Visit your dentist twice a year. Once you have your **permanent** teeth they are friends meant to last a lifetime!

Page 98

---

Pretend that you are in a movie theater. List objects that your senses might notice.

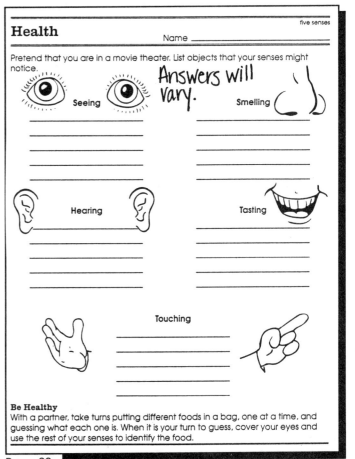

Answers will vary.

Seeing

Smelling

Hearing

Tasting

Touching

**Be Healthy**
With a partner, take turns putting different foods in a bag, one at a time, and guessing what each one is. When it is your turn to guess, cover your eyes and use the rest of your senses to identify the food.

Page 99

---

Name _____

substances

Make a mini-poster for each substance described below. Write the name of the substance below its matching poster.

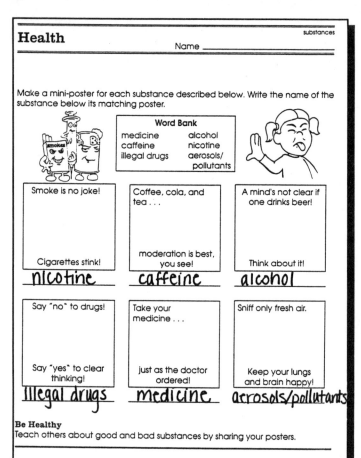

**Word Bank**

| medicine | alcohol |
| caffeine | nicotine |
| illegal drugs | aerosols/ pollutants |

| Smoke is no joke! | Coffee, cola, and tea . . . | A mind's not clear if one drinks beer! |
| --- | --- | --- |
| Cigarettes stink! | moderation is best, you see! | Think about it! |
| **nicotine** | **caffeine** | **alcohol** |

| Say "no" to drugs! | Take your medicine . . . | Sniff only fresh air. |
| --- | --- | --- |
| Say "yes" to clear thinking! | just as the doctor ordered! | Keep your lungs and brain happy! |
| **illegal drugs** | **medicine** | **aerosols/pollutants** |

**Be Healthy**
Teach others about good and bad substances by sharing your posters.

---

Name _____

safety

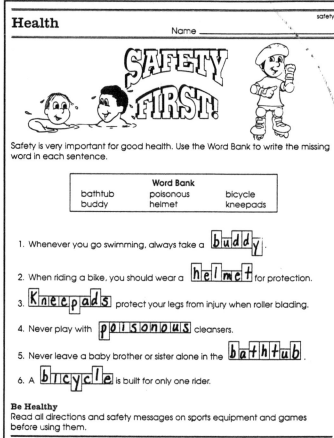

Safety is very important for good health. Use the Word Bank to write the missing word in each sentence.

**Word Bank**

| bathtub | poisonous | bicycle |
| buddy | helmet | kneepads |

1. Whenever you go swimming, always take a **buddy**.

2. When riding a bike, you should wear a **helmet** for protection.

3. **Kneepads** protect your legs from injury when roller blading.

4. Never play with **poisonous** cleansers.

5. Never leave a baby brother or sister alone in the **bathtub**.

6. A **bicycle** is built for only one rider.

**Be Healthy**
Read all directions and safety messages on sports equipment and games before using them.

---

Name _____

healthy hints

Use the clue to solve each related health/safety situation. Write the answers on the lines.

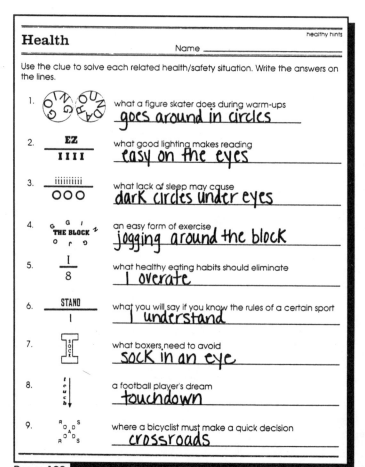

1. what a figure skater does during warm-ups
   **goes around in circles**

2. what good lighting makes reading
   **easy on the eyes**

3. what lack of sleep may cause
   **dark circles under eyes**

4. an easy form of exercise
   **jogging around the block**

5. what healthy eating habits should eliminate
   **I overate**

6. what you will say if you know the rules of a certain sport
   **I understand**

7. what boxers need to avoid
   **sock in an eye**

8. a football player's dream
   **touchdown**

9. where a bicyclist must make a quick decision
   **crossroads**

---

## About the Book

This is a great activity book which can be used in the spring for review, or in the summer or fall to brush up on skills from the previous year. The author has used a variety of activities which every child will enjoy while reviewing Language Arts, Math, Health and Science and Social Studies.

## Credits

**Author:** Cindy Karwowski
**Artist:** Chris Olsen
**Project Director/Editor:** Sue Sutton
**Editors:** Alyson Kieda, Sue Vanderlaan
**\*Cover Photo:** Frank Pieroni
**Production:** Pat Geasler

*Cover photo taken of the Rounds School in Rockford, MI. Permission to use given by the Rockford Rotary Club.

---